Dangerous Substances and Explosive Atmospheres

Dangerous Substances and Explosive Atmospheres Regulations 2002

APPROVED CODE OF PRACTICE AND GUIDANCE

HSEBOOKS

This Code has been approved by the Health and Safety Commission, with the consent of the Secretary of State. It gives practical advice on how to comply with the law. If you follow the advice you will be doing enough to comply with the law in respect of those specific matters on which the Code gives advice. You may use alternative methods to those set out in the Code in order to comply with the law.

However, the Code has special legal status. If you are prosecuted for breach of health and safety law, and it is proved that you did not follow the relevant provisions of the Code, you will need to show that you have complied with the law in some other way or a court will find you at fault.

The Regulations and the Approved Code of Practice (ACOP) are accompanied by guidance which does not form part of the ACOP. Following the guidance is not compulsory and you are free to take other action. But if you do follow the guidance you will normally be doing enough to comply with the law. Health and Safety inspectors seek to secure compliance with the law and may refer to this guidance as illustrating good practice.

Contents

This publication contains the Dangerous Substances and Explosive Atmospheres Regulations,[1] together with an Approved Code of Practice and supporting guidance.

For convenience, the text of the Regulations is set out in *italic* type, with the ACOP in **bold** type and the accompanying guidance in normal type.

Notice of Approval

By virtue of section 16(1) of the Health and Safety at Work etc Act 1974 and with the consent of the Secretary of State for Work and Pensions, the Health and Safety Commission has on 5 August 2003 approved the Code of Practice entitled *Dangerous substances and explosive atmospheres*.

The Code of Practice gives practical guidance with respect to the Dangerous Substances and Explosive Atmospheres Regulations 2002.

The Code of Practice comes into effect on 8 December 2003.

Signed

Mark Dempsey
Secretary to the Health and Safety Commission
3 October 2003

Introduction

1   The Dangerous Substances and Explosive Atmospheres Regulations 2002[1] (DSEAR) are concerned with protection against risks from fire, explosion and similar events arising from dangerous substances used or present in the workplace. They set minimum requirements for the protection of workers from fire and explosion risks related to dangerous substances and potentially explosive atmospheres. The Regulations apply to employers and the self-employed at most workplaces in Great Britain where a dangerous substance is present or could be present.

2   DSEAR revokes, repeals or modifies a large amount of old legislation relating to flammable substances and dusts. Safety standards will be maintained through a combination of the requirements of DSEAR and Approved Codes of Practice (ACOPs) reflecting good practices in the old legislation.[2-6]

3   The key requirements in DSEAR are that risks from dangerous substances are assessed and eliminated or reduced. This publication provides interpretive ACOP and guidance and is part of a series of publications intended to support DSEAR. Other activity-related ACOP and guidance material is available in the following publications:

(a)   *Design of plant, equipment and workplaces*[2] - This gives practical advice on assessing the risk from, and the design and use of, plant, equipment and workplaces which handle or process dangerous substances. It includes measures for making redundant plant and equipment safe.

(b)   *Storage of dangerous substances*[3] - This gives practical advice on the requirements of regulation 5 and 6 to assess the risks from, and the control and mitigation measures for, places where dangerous substances are stored. It includes the safe disposal of waste materials.

(c)   *Control and mitigation measures*[4] - This gives practical advice on the requirements of regulation 5 and 6 to identify the hazards arising from the dangerous substance and put in place adequate ventilation, ignition control and separation measures to control risks.

(d)   *Safe maintenance, repair and cleaning procedures*[5] - This gives practical advice on identifying hazards and implementing appropriate control measures and systems of work during maintenance and other similar non-routine activities. It includes advice on hot work and on permit-to-work systems for those activities identified as high risk.

(e)   *Unloading petrol from road tankers*[6] - This gives practical advice and details the measures necessary in respect of regulation 6 with regard to the safe unloading of petrol tankers at petrol filling stations.

4   In addition, the free leaflet *Fire and explosion: How safe is your workplace?*[7] provides a short guide to DSEAR and is aimed at small and medium-sized businesses.

5   Information on DSEAR can also be accessed via HSE's website: www.hse.gov.uk, which is regularly updated.

The legislative background

6   The Dangerous Substances and Explosive Atmospheres Regulations 2002[1] (DSEAR) were made under the Health and Safety at Work etc Act 1974[8] (HSW Act) and their main provisions came into force on 9 December 2002. The Regulations apply to workplaces (as defined in regulation 2) in Great Britain. These workplaces, which cover most sectors of industry and commerce, are also subject to the HSW Act. A limited number of requirements concern explosive atmospheres and these came into force on 30 June 2003, their application is subject to transitional arrangements.

7   The Regulations implement two European Directives: the safety aspects of the Chemical Agents Directive[(a)] 98/24/EC[9] (CAD) and the Explosive Atmospheres Directive 99/92/EC[10] (ATEX 137) requiring similar legislation throughout the European Union (EU) on work involving hazardous chemical agents and explosive atmospheres.

8   This publication contains an Approved Code of Practice and guidance on the duties in DSEAR. It has been prepared by the Health and Safety Executive for the Health and Safety Commission after consultation with stakeholders in industry, trade unions, local authorities and fire authorities.

Summary of the Regulations

9   The primary purpose of DSEAR is to protect the safety of workers and others who may be at risk from dangerous substances that can cause a fire, explosion or similar energy-releasing event, such as a runaway exothermic reaction. The Regulations are set out as follows:

- Regulations 1 to 4 deal with preliminary issues, ie the date of entry into force of the Regulations, scope and definitions.

- Regulation 5 requires employers and the self-employed to assess risks to employees and others whose safety may be affected by the use or presence of dangerous substances at work.

- Regulation 6 sets out how the risk to safety from dangerous substances should be eliminated or reduced.

- Regulation 7 contains specific requirements to be applied where an explosive atmosphere may be present (in addition to the requirements in regulation 6).

- Regulation 8 requires the provision of arrangements to deal with accidents, incidents and emergencies.

- Regulation 9 requires the provision of information, training and instruction on dangerous substances.

- Regulation 10 requires the identification of pipes and containers where these contain dangerous substances.

- Regulation 11 addresses the need to coordinate explosion protection measures where employers share the same workplace.

(a) The health aspects of CAD are implemented separately through the Control of Substances Hazardous to Health Regulations 2002, the Control of Lead at Work Regulations 2002 and the Control of Asbestos at Work Regulations 2002.

- Regulations 12-16 deal with the application of the Regulations outside Great Britain, exemptions from the Regulations, and amendments to and removal of other legislation.

- Regulation 17 sets out the transitional arrangements for workplaces and work equipment where explosive atmospheres may occur.

Relationship with other health and safety legislation

10   The duties in DSEAR apply alongside the HSW Act and other Regulations made under the Act, and also legislation on fire precautions. The following paragraphs explain the interface between DSEAR and some key pieces of legislation.

The Management of Health and Safety at Work Regulations 1999

11   The Management of Health and Safety at Work Regulations 1999[11] (MHSW Regulations) support the general duties in the HSW Act.[8] The MHSW Regulations require employers and the self-employed, among other things, to: assess the general risks to health and safety arising from their work activity; identify the preventive and protective measures that need to be taken to control the identified risks; introduce procedures for serious and imminent danger; and to provide information and training for employees.

12   Where dangerous substances are present or used at the workplace the more specific provisions of DSEAR will apply to work with those substances. For example, an assessment of the risks from dangerous substances carried out under DSEAR will not need to be repeated for the MHSW Regulations,[11] and in many cases will be incorporated into the more general MHSW Regulations assessment. Similarly, the provisions in DSEAR concerning arrangements for emergencies involving dangerous substances will cover much of the same ground as the corresponding general requirements for such procedures in the MHSW Regulations.

Fire precautions legislation

13   Workplace fire precautions legislation, including the Fire Precautions Act 1971[12] and the Fire Precautions (Workplace) Regulations 1997 (amended 1999) (FPW Regulations)[13] deal with means of detection and giving warning in case of fire; the provision of means of escape; means of fighting fire; and the training of staff in fire safety. Regulation 3(1) of the MHSW Regulations[11] includes a requirement to undertake an assessment of fire risks.

14   DSEAR amends the FPW Regulations[13] to make specific provisions of DSEAR (regulations 1-6, 8, 9 and 11) part of the workplace fire precautions legislation. This means that fire authorities have enforcement responsibility for those parts of DSEAR to the extent that they concern general fire precautions.

The Control of Substances Hazardous to Health Regulations 2002

15   Health risks from substances are primarily controlled by the Control of Substances Hazardous to Health Regulations 2002[14] (COSHH). Health effects relating to lead and asbestos are covered by the Control of Lead at Work Regulations 2002 (CLAW)[15] and the Control of Asbestos at Work Regulations 2002 (CAWR)[16] respectively.

16   The definitions of 'dangerous substance' and 'substance hazardous to health' contained in DSEAR and COSHH[14] respectively, cover a wide range of substances. As a result, most substances that may be dangerous to safety will also present a health risk.

17   For example, certain gases (hydrogen, methane, propane, etc) are extremely flammable and come within the scope of DSEAR. However, the gases themselves can also act as asphyxiants, reducing the quantity of oxygen present in a workplace to the extent that life can be put at risk. As a result, they will also satisfy the definition of a substance hazardous to health for the purposes of COSHH.[14] In these circumstances, employers will have duties to control the risks from those substances under both sets of Regulations.

18   To meet the requirements of both DSEAR and COSHH,[14] employers will need to consider and put in place practical measures for achieving the overall protection of the health and safety of their employees and other people who may be put at risk from dangerous substances.

The Confined Spaces Regulations 1997

19   The Confined Spaces Regulations 1997 (CSR)[17] apply to work in confined spaces in all premises and work situations except for diving operations; below ground in a mine; offshore installations (except when moored at the dockside or stacked for repair); wells; pipelines; offshore mines; and in respect of normal ship-board activities carried out solely by the crew.

20   There are many cases where dangerous substances within the scope of DSEAR may be present in confined spaces. For example: fuel in large storage tanks during cleaning or repair activities within the vessel; flammable waste products in bunds; and chemically unstable substances in process vessels. Dangerous substances (for example, in the form of gases) can accumulate in confined spaces and form explosive concentrations that can ignite causing severe injuries and even without ignition may act as asphyxiants.

21   Where work involving a dangerous substance takes place in a confined space, the requirements of CSR[17] will apply in addition to the requirements of DSEAR.

The Equipment and Protective Systems Intended for Use in Potentially Explosive Atmospheres Regulations 1996

22   The Equipment and Protective Systems Intended for Use in Potentially Explosive Atmospheres Regulations 1996 as amended (EPS),[18] implement Directive 94/9/EC[19] (commonly referred to as 'the ATEX product Directive'). EPS applies to both electrical and mechanical equipment and protective systems intended for use in potentially explosive atmospheres. Responsible persons have been able to place such equipment on the European market since 1 March 1996. The requirements of the EPS Regulations have become mandatory for all such equipment and protective systems that are placed on the market or put into service in the EU for the first time after 30 June 2003.

23   New equipment, etc, supplied for use in places where an explosive atmosphere may occur must meet the requirements of the EPS Regulations[18] whether it is provided by a manufacturer, authorised representative or importer or whether employers manufacture or import equipment themselves.

24   Second-hand equipment and equipment already on the shelf (for example, as spares) before 1 July 2003 that has already been placed on the

market or used within the EU does not have to meet the requirements of the EPS Regulations[18] (provided it does not need any substantial modification) but must nonetheless be safe for use in an explosive atmosphere.

The Provision and Use of Work Equipment Regulations 1998

25   The Provision and Use of Work Equipment Regulations 1998 as amended (PUWER)[20] require employers, the self-employed and people in control to provide safe work equipment, to use it safely, and to maintain it. PUWER also requires that when first providing work equipment for use in the workplace employers should ensure that it has been made to the requirements of any legislation implementing any relevant product Directives such as the ATEX Directive 94/9/EC,[19] implemented through the EPS Regulations.[18]

26   After 30 June 2003, compliance with DSEAR with regard to the selection of equipment etc in accordance with the EPS Regulations[18] will be enough to satisfy this requirement in PUWER.[20] DSEAR also places a duty on employers to maintain equipment etc, and compliance with this requirement will satisfy a corresponding general requirement in PUWER with regard to equipment used in connection with dangerous substances or explosive atmospheres.

The Personal Protective Equipment Regulations 1992

27   The supply of health and safety equipment comes under the Personal Protective Equipment Regulations 1992.[21] Under these Regulations employers must select, provide and maintain appropriate equipment for employees whenever risks are not adequately protected against by other means. Employers should also provide information, training and instruction for employees on its use and maintenance. All equipment provided under these or other Regulations must be provided without charge to employees.

The Petroleum (Consolidation) Act 1928[22] and associated Regulations

28   DSEAR amends the workplace application of petrol safety legislation so that licensing applies only at sites, which dispense petrol into vehicles, ships, boats and planes. Other sites storing petrol for other purposes, such as factories etc, will no longer require petrol licences but will need to comply with DSEAR.

29   HSE is undertaking a review of petrol legislation, but at the moment both petrol licensing and DSEAR will apply at petrol filling stations. DSEAR does not apply to sites that are not workplaces; therefore the current legislation concerning the storage of petrol in domestic premises remains in place.

Legislation on consulting employees and safety representatives

30   Proper consultation with those who do the work is crucial to raise awareness of the importance of health and safety. It can make a significant contribution to creating and maintaining a safe and healthy working environment and an effective health and safety culture. In turn, this can benefit the business by making it more efficient by reducing the number of accidents and the incidents of work-related ill health.

31   Employers must consult safety representatives appointed by recognised trade unions under the Safety Representatives and Safety Committees Regulations 1997.[23] Employees who are not covered by such representatives must be consulted either directly or indirectly, through elected representatives

of employee safety under the Health and Safety (Consultation with Employees) Regulations 1996.[24] More information on employers' duties under these Regulations is contained in the free HSE leaflet *Consulting employees on health and safety: A guide to the law.*[25]

DSEAR and other legislation on dangerous substances or hazardous activities

32   Subject to regulation 3(1), risks from dangerous substances or explosive atmospheres may also be subject to other specific legislation dealing with, for example:

(a)   risks from major hazard activities, covered by the Control of Major Accident Hazards Regulations 1999 (COMAH);[26]

(b)   the prevention of fires and explosions offshore through the Offshore Installations (Prevention of Fire and Explosion, and Emergency Response) Regulations 1995 (PFEER)[27] or the Offshore Installations and Pipeline Works (Management and Administration) Regulations 1995;[28] and

(c)   the transport of dangerous goods, covered by specific carriage legislation, such as the Carriage of Dangerous Goods by Road Regulations 1996 (CDG).[29]

33   The above list is not exclusive and other legislation includes provisions on preventing fires and explosions for example in quarries, mines or harbour areas. In many cases, compliance with the specific requirements of such other legislation will go a long way towards meeting the requirements of DSEAR.

Environmental issues

34   DSEAR deals with risks to people from dangerous substances. It should be recognised that such substances could also pose a threat to the environment, for example, through disposal or in the event of a spill. In undertaking any risk assessment, or developing emergency arrangements, the potential for environmental harm should also be considered. Further guidance on this may be obtained from, the Environment Agency (EA) in England and Wales, and the Scottish Environment Protection Agency (SEPA) in Scotland. A guidance publication – *Pollution Prevention Guidance Note 21 – Pollution response planning*[30] is also available free of charge.

Repeals, revocations and amendments

35   DSEAR replaces or modernises a large number of pieces of old legislation on flammable substances including the Highly Flammable Liquids and Liquefied Petroleum Gases Regulations 1972[31] and section 31 of the Factories Act 1961.[32] The Regulations also amend petrol safety legislation to restrict its application to retail petrol stations and the storage of petrol in domestic premises.

Enforcement arrangements

36   DSEAR is enforced by HSE and local authority inspectors in accordance with the Health and Safety (Enforcing Authority) Regulations 1998;[33] except at retail petrol stations. At these premises the Regulations are enforced by petroleum licensing authorities (PLAs) in respect of any activities related to fuelling motor vehicles with petrol or any other dangerous substance, such as

liquefied petroleum gas. PLAs enforce the dispensing of petrol, but not other fuels, at non-retail petrol filling stations. In addition, at the majority of workplaces, fire authorities will enforce those parts of DSEAR that relate to general fire precautions.

Citation and commencement

These Regulations may be cited as the Dangerous Substances and Explosive Atmospheres Regulations 2002 and shall come into force -

> (a) *as respects all regulations except for regulations 5(4)(c), 7, 11, 15(2), 16(2) and 17(1) to (3) on 9th December 2002;*

> (b) *as respects regulations 15(2) and 16(2) on 5th May 2003; and*

> (c) *as respects regulations 5(4)(c), 7, 11 and 17(1) to (3) on 30th June 2003.*

37   These Regulations came into force on 9 December 2002, (except regulations 15(2) and 16(2), which came into force on 5 May 2003 and amend and repeal certain old pieces of legislation).

38   In addition, some requirements relating specifically to the presence of explosive atmospheres in the workplace came into effect on 30 June 2003. These relate to:

(a)   certain information relating to the presence of explosive atmospheres to be included in employers' risk assessments (regulation 5(4)(c));

(b)   classifying those places where explosive atmospheres may be present (regulation 7(1));

(c)   ensuring that requirements relating to the equipment and protective systems are applied in places classified into zones (regulation 7(2));

(d)   marking the points of entry to places where explosive atmospheres may be present (regulation 7(3));

(e)   verifying the overall explosion safety of a workplace before it is used for the first time (regulation 7(4));

(f)   providing appropriate work clothing that does not give rise to electrostatic discharges (regulation 7(5));

(g)   a duty on employers responsible for a shared workplace to co-ordinate the implementation of measures to protect employees from the risks presented by explosive atmospheres (regulation 11);

(h)   transitional provisions relating to equipment to be used in explosive atmospheres and workplaces where such atmospheres may be present (regulation 17).

Interpretation

In these Regulations-

"approved classification and labelling guide" means the "Approved Guide to the Classification and Labelling of Dangerous Substances and Dangerous Preparations " (5th edition)[a] approved by the Health and Safety Commission on 16th April 2002;

"the CHIP Regulations" means the Chemicals (Hazard Information and Packaging for Supply) Regulations 2002[b];

"dangerous substance" means -

(a) *a substance or preparation which meets the criteria in the approved classification and labelling guide for classification as a substance or preparation which is explosive, oxidising, extremely flammable, highly flammable or flammable, whether or not that substance or preparation is classified under the CHIP Regulations;*

(b) *a substance or preparation which because of its physico-chemical or chemical properties and the way it is used or is present at the workplace creates a risk, not being a substance or preparation falling within subparagraph (a) above; or*

(c) *any dust, whether in the form of solid particles or fibrous materials or otherwise, which can form an explosive mixture with air or an explosive atmosphere, not being a substance or preparation falling within subparagraphs (a) or (b) above;*

"explosive atmosphere" means a mixture, under atmospheric conditions, of air and one or more dangerous substances in the form of gases, vapours, mists or dusts in which, after ignition has occurred, combustion spreads to the entire unburned mixture;

"hazard" means the physico-chemical or chemical property of a dangerous substance which has the potential to give rise to fire, explosion, or other events which can result in harmful physical effects of a kind similar to those which can be caused by fire or explosion, affecting the safety of a person, and references in these Regulations to "hazardous" shall be construed accordingly;

"offshore installation" has the same meaning as it is given by regulation 3 of the Offshore Installations and Pipeline Works (Management and Administration) Regulations 1995[c] insofar as that regulation extends to mineral extracting industries within the scope of Article 2(a) of Council Directive 92/91/EEC concerning the minimum requirements for improving the safety and health protection of workers in the mineral-extracting industries through drilling[d];

"personal protective equipment" means all equipment which is intended to be worn or held by a person at work and which protects that person against one or more risks to his safety, and any addition or accessory designed to meet that objective;

"preparation" means a mixture or solution of two or more substances;

(a) ISBN 0 7176 2369 6
(b) S.I. 2002/1689
(c) S.I. 1995/738
(d) OJ No L348, 28.11.92, p.9

"*public road*" means (in England and Wales) a highway maintainable at public expense within the meaning of section 329 of the Highways Act 1980[a] and (in Scotland) a public road within the meaning assigned to that term by section 151 of the Roads (Scotland) Act 1984[b];

"*risk*" means the likelihood of a person's safety being affected by harmful physical effects being caused to him from fire, explosion or other events arising from the hazardous properties of a dangerous substance in connection with work and also the extent of that harm;

"*risk assessment*" means the assessment of risks required by regulation 5(1);

"*safety data sheet*" means a safety data sheet within the meaning of regulation 5 of the CHIP Regulations;

"*substance*" means any natural or artificial substance whether in solid or liquid form or in the form of a gas or vapour;

"*workplace*" means any premises or part of premises used for or in connection with work, and includes -

    (a)   any place within the premises to which an employee has access while at work; and

    (b)   any room, lobby, corridor, staircase, road or other place -

        (i)   used as a means of access to or egress from that place of work, or,

        (ii)   where facilities are provided for use in connection with that place of work,

other than a public road; and

"*work processes*" means all technical aspects of work involving dangerous substances and includes -

    (a)   appropriate technical means of supervision,

    (b)   connecting devices,

    (c)   control and protection systems,

    (d)   engineering controls and solutions,

    (e)   equipment,

    (f)   materials,

    (g)   machinery,

    (h)   plant,

    (i)   protective systems, and

    (j)   warning and other communication systems.

(a) 1980 c.66
(b) 1984 c.54

Dangerous substances

39   The Regulations apply wherever a dangerous substance is, or is liable to be, present at the workplace. Dangerous substances include substances, preparations and dusts with the potential to give rise to fires, explosions and similar energetic (energy releasing) events (such as runaway exothermic reactions) which can affect the safety of employees and others.

40   Although the chemical and petroleum industries will by their very nature store, use and process the majority of dangerous substances, most other sectors, such as manufacturing, food, retailing, etc will also have dangerous substances present - but possibly in small quantities.

41   Examples of dangerous substances include: petrol, liquefied petroleum gas (LPG), paints, varnishes and certain types of dusts produced in, for example, machining and sanding operations.

42   In general terms, to determine whether dangerous substances are present in the workplace, employers will need to carry out the following three steps-

Step 1 - Check whether the substance or preparation has been classified under the Chemicals (Hazard Information and Packaging for Supply) Regulations[34] (CHIP) as: explosive, oxidising, extremely flammable, highly flammable or flammable.

Step 2 - Assess the physical and chemical properties of the substance or preparation and the work processes involved to see whether the work activity creates a potential for fire, explosion or similar energetic (energy releasing) event.

Step 3 - Check to see if the work activity involves the creation or handling of potentially combustible or explosive dusts.

Step 1

43   The CHIP Regulations[34] require dangerous substances to be classified by suppliers using criteria set out in the *Approved guide to the classification and labelling of substances and preparations dangerous for supply*[35] into certain categories of danger such as 'extremely flammable'.

44   When dangerous chemicals are used at work, suppliers must provide safety data sheets which tell employers whether the chemical is classified as oxidising, flammable etc.

45   Another source of information is the *Approved supply list. Information approved for the classification and labelling of substances and preparations dangerous for supply,*[36] which is produced by HSE and lists many commonly used substances and their classification.

46   If a substance or preparation is classified as explosive, oxidising, extremely flammable, highly flammable or flammable then it is a 'dangerous substance'.

Step 2

47   Although a substance or preparation may not be caught under Step 1, it may still be considered to be dangerous for the purposes of these Regulations.

48   Firstly, it may be that the properties of the substance or preparation are such that it meets the technical criteria for classification, but is exempt from CHIP.[34] For example, a flammable solvent produced in a chemical process and then used again in another process on the same premises is exempt from CHIP. No labelling or provision of safety data sheets needs to be carried out. However, if that substance meets the technical criteria for 'flammability' in the approved guide, DSEAR applies even though CHIP does not.

49   If a substance or preparation meets the criteria for classification as set out in the approved guide, it is a 'dangerous substance' even if it is exempt from CHIP.[34]

50   Secondly, the Regulations may apply because of the way a substance or preparation is used or present. For example, diesel oil is not classified as flammable under CHIP.[34] Nevertheless, its physical properties are such that when heated to a high temperature it can present a fire risk. If there was such a process in the employer's premises then DSEAR applies.

51   The key point is that it is not only the substance's fundamental physical or chemical properties, but also the way the substance or preparation is used/processed or present that determines whether DSEAR applies. If, in the above example, diesel was present on the premises but was only in store, then DSEAR would not apply to that storage activity because it is likely to be stored below its flashpoint.

52   Another example would be substances which on their own or when mixed with others decompose or react to release energy such that there could be a fire or explosion. Examples include certain chemical reactions with the potential for thermal runaway and the handling and storage of unstable substances such as certain types of peroxides.

53   For Step 2, therefore, employers will need to carry out a risk assessment using information about the physical and chemical properties of the substance or preparation and the characteristics of the work processes to determine whether there is a hazard and risk (see also definition of these terms).

54   If the assessment of the work activity involving the substance or preparation shows that there is a risk of a fire, explosion or similar energetic event then the substance or preparation is a 'dangerous substance'.

Step 3

55   The dusts of many combustible materials in everyday use such as coal, wood, grain, flour, sugar, certain metals and synthetic organic chemicals, when dispersed in air to form a cloud (ie form an explosive atmosphere - see definition and guidance below) can explode if an ignition source is present. Documented records of such explosions go back over 100 years and some incidents have caused large loss of life.

56   CHIP[34] will not tell employers whether they have an explosive dust present at the workplace. Determining whether DSEAR applies requires knowledge of the physical and chemical characteristics of the substance and an assessment of the processes forming or handling the dust - particularly the size of dust particles being produced or handled. Further information on how to assess the risks of combustible and explosive dusts and the relevant safety precautions are contained in HSE publication *Safe handling of combustible dusts*[37] and in the software program *Dust expert*.[38]

11

57   If dusts that can form an explosive atmosphere are used or present they are defined as a 'dangerous substance' under the Regulations.

Particular points to note

58   Substances and preparations are potentially within the scope of the Regulations - whether in solid, liquid or gaseous form. This includes substances that are naturally occurring or produced in a chemical or manufacturing process. Substances are also included if they are produced by a work activity - for example intermediates in a chemical process, waste products of any kind, or substances produced in accident conditions eg in a runaway chemical reaction.

59   If there is a substance or preparation present that is dangerous, DSEAR applies.

Explosive atmospheres

60   This definition sets out the criteria to determine whether an atmosphere is explosive within the scope of the Regulations. The definition is particularly important in deciding when certain requirements in DSEAR will apply, particularly regulations 7, 11 and 17.

61   'Explosive atmosphere' is also defined in the EPS Regulations.[18]

62   The following guidance is consistent with the guidance on the EPS Regulations.[18] For the purposes of DSEAR the following elements must all be present for an explosive atmosphere to form.

Atmospheric conditions

63   'Atmospheric conditions' are commonly referred to as ambient temperature and pressure. For the purposes of standardisation, atmospheric conditions are defined as follows: -20 to 40°C, and 0.8 to 1.1 bar. Any equipment manufacturer who wants to build equipment then has to demonstrate that the equipment will operate safely throughout this range of temperature and pressure. Where a process operates outside this range, the risk of fire and explosion may still exist, but a more detailed assessment of the process and equipment to be used is likely to be needed, and regulations 7, 11 and 17 do not apply. However, it should be stressed that regulation 6 will require such a process to be made safe.

Mixtures of air and dangerous substances

64   An explosive atmosphere must include air and one or more dangerous substances defined in regulation 2 above. The dangerous substances can be in the form of a gas, vapour, mist or dust. Dangerous substances or mixtures of such substances, that are explosive with an oxidant other than air, for example pure oxygen or chlorine, are outside the scope of the definition of explosive atmosphere and the provisions of regulations 7, 11 and 17 do not apply although other requirements in DSEAR may do.

Combustion

65   The definition is intended to make clear that where it can be ensured that the gas or dust is present in a concentration below the lower flammable limit, the atmosphere is not explosive, and regulations 7, 11 and 17 do not apply. In this guidance, the terms 'lower (or higher) flammable limit' is intended to mean the same as 'lower (or higher) explosive limit'.

Hazard

66   In general terms a hazard means anything that can cause harm eg chemicals, electricity, working at height on ladders etc.

67   These Regulations place a more restricted meaning to this general term in relation to those dangerous substances and preparations that have the potential to create fires or explosions and similar energetic events.

68   The definition is best understood by looking at its parts.

Harmful physical effects of a kind similar to those caused by fire or explosion

69   The Regulations are concerned with dangerous substances that can create harmful physical effects. Health effects from substances and preparations are not within the scope of DSEAR and are dealt with by health legislation such as COSHH.[14]

70   However, DSEAR is not intended to address all possible physical effects, such as crushing injuries, resulting, for example, from the storage and handling of heavy containers of dangerous substances and preparations. The Regulations are intended to cover only the following harmful physical effects caused directly or indirectly by fires and explosions:

(a)   thermal radiation effects (burns);

(b)   over-pressure effects (blast injuries);

(c)   oxygen depletion effects (asphyxiation).

Fires, explosions or other events

71   Fires and explosions can cause thermal radiation, over-pressure effects and oxygen depletion, but these harmful physical effects can also be caused by other energetic events such as runaway exothermic reactions or decompositions of unstable substances - for example, decomposition of peroxides. These words are included in the definition to ensure that not only fires and explosions are covered, but also other similar energetic events.

Physico-chemical or chemical property

72   Ultimately the hazard is created by the physical and chemical properties of the substance or preparation and the way it is used or present in the workplace.

73   Examples of relevant physical properties include: boiling point, flash-point, auto-ignition temperature, flammability, vapour pressure, thermal sensitivity, mechanical sensitivity and oxidising properties. Relevant chemical properties would include reactivity, heat of reaction and self-acceleration decomposition temperature. Other properties of substances relating to radioactivity, toxicity and ecotoxicity are not within the scope of the Regulations. Test methods to determine physico-chemical properties are detailed in Annex V of EU Directive 67/548/EEC[39] and can be found on the European Chemicals Bureau website at http//ecb.jrc.it (testing methods).

74   For materials that could give rise to a dust explosion, factors such as the particle size and moisture content will effect the explosion properties. The

maximum explosion pressure and maximum rate of pressure rise of a dust are important in assessing the risk. These properties are measured in a standard test apparatus. See BS 6713,[40] which is currently under revision (see prEN 14034[41]).

Risk

75   Risk is the chance, high or low, that someone will be harmed by the hazard. For the purposes of these Regulations the definition of 'risk' builds on the definition of hazard and ensures that the risks addressed are those created by the physical and chemical properties of substances and preparations which can lead to fires, explosions and similar energetic events; and, in turn, lead to the harmful physical effects mentioned above, and the extent of the harm. Other risks such as risks to health, crushing risks etc are not within the scope of the Regulations.

Workplace

76   The definition of 'workplace' is based on that used in the Workplace (Health, Safety and Welfare) Regulations 1992.[42] It is however wider in scope as it also includes domestic premises - ie areas in private dwellings where work is carried out.

77   The term 'premises', used in the definition of 'workplace', means any place - whether or not there is a structure at that place. It includes, subject to the disapplications in regulation 3, vehicles, vessels, any land-based or offshore installations, movable areas to which employees have access while at work and their means of access to and egress from, the workplace. Thus, common parts of shared buildings, private roads and paths on industrial estates and business parks are included.

78   Public roads, which are used to get to or from the workplace, are not included in the definition. However, in some circumstances, a public road may itself become the workplace, and if dangerous substances are used or produced during the work activity concerned, these Regulations may apply, for example during road repairing or work on utilities.

79   Subject to the disapplications in regulation 3, these Regulations apply whenever a dangerous substance is present at the workplace. It therefore has a very wide scope and includes nearly every commercial and industrial sector, both onshore and offshore within Great Britain. Subject to regulation 14, dangerous substances in workplaces under the control of the Ministry of Defence are also covered. Docks, harbours and naval bases are also within the definition of workplace.

80   The Regulations apply to all work activities eg storage, processing, packaging, and warehousing carried out within a workplace. Other examples include maintenance, repairing and cleaning activities.

81   Subject to certain disapplications in regulation 3, transport of dangerous substances by road and rail are also within the scope of the Regulations. The Chemical Agents Directive (CAD),[9] which these Regulations implement, applies to the transport of dangerous goods on inland waterways and by sea in GB waters. However these requirements, with one exception, are being addressed by regulations being developed by the Marine and Coastguard Agency. The exception concerns Royal Navy ships when in GB waters.

82   The Regulations also apply to domestic premises provided there is a

work activity involving dangerous substances being carried out there either by an employer or a self-employed person (see regulation 4).

83　The Regulations do not apply in Northern Ireland for which separate legislation has been developed.

Work processes

84　This means the 'hardware' aspects of work involving dangerous substances that are of a technical nature eg gas detectors, flameproof enclosures, regulating devices. It excludes systems of work, eg management and non-technical supervisory arrangements, but does include appropriate technical means of supervision.

85　Technical means of supervision are those technical measures that are required by the risk assessment to prevent employees from working in or entering an explosive atmosphere. They will include monitoring and interlock devices that are designed to stop a process or alert an employee in the event of a mechanical fault, procedural error or foreseeable process deviation that could result in the formation of a hazardous explosive atmosphere. Examples of such technical measures include:

(a)　gas monitoring and alarm systems for employees working in confined spaces where flammable vapours may be present or released by the activity;

(b)　interlocks on coating operations that would stop the application of flammable coating products if the associated mechanical exhaust ventilation is interrupted.

Technical means of supervision may be used as a separate supervisory function or as part of a wider management system for controlling risks.

Regulation 3

Application

(1)　These Regulations, apart from regulations 15, 16 and 17(4) to (5), shall not apply to the master or crew of a ship or to the employer of such persons in respect of the normal ship-board activities of a ship's crew which are carried out solely by the crew under the direction of the master and, for the purposes of this paragraph -

(a)　"ship" includes every description of vessel used in navigation, other than a ship forming part of Her Majesty's Navy or an offshore installation; and

(b)　the reference to the normal ship-board activities of a ship's crew includes -

(i)　the construction, reconstruction or conversion of a ship outside, but not inside, Great Britain; and

(ii)　the repair of a ship save repair when carried out in dry dock.

(2)　Regulations 5(4)(c), 7 and 11 shall not apply to -

(a)　areas used directly for and during the medical treatment of patients;

(b)　the use of gas appliances burning gaseous fuel (that is to say, any fuel which is in a gaseous state at a temperature of 15°C under a pressure of 1 bar) which -

15

(i)   are used for cooking, heating, hot water production, refrigeration, lighting or washing; and

(ii)   have, where applicable, a normal water temperature not exceeding 105°C

including forced draught burners and heating bodies to be equipped with such burners but not including an appliance specifically designed for use in an industrial process carried out on industrial premises;

(c)   gas fittings within the meaning of the Gas Safety (Installation and Use) Regulations 1998[(a)] located in domestic premises, not being gas appliances falling within subparagraph (b);

(d)   the manufacture, handling, use, storage and transport of explosives or chemically unstable substances;

(e)   any activity at a mine within the meaning of section 180 of the Mines and Quarries Act 1954[(b)] carried out for the purposes of the mine;

(f)   any activity at a quarry within the meaning of regulation 3 of the Quarries Regulations 1999[(c)] carried out for the purposes of the quarry;

(g)   any activity at a borehole site within the meaning of regulation 2(1) of the Borehole Sites and Operations Regulations 1995[(d)] carried out for the purposes of the borehole site;

(h)   any activity at an offshore installation carried out for the purposes of the offshore installation; and

(i)   the use of means of transport by land, water or air which is regulated by international agreements and the European Community Directives giving effect to them insofar as they fall within the disapplication in Article 1.2.(e) of Council Directive 99/92/EC on minimum requirements for improving the safety and health protection of workers potentially at risk from explosive atmospheres[(e)], except for any means of transport intended for use in a potentially explosive atmosphere.

(3)   Regulations 5(2)(f), (g), (h) and (i), 6(4)(d), 6(5)(b) and (e) and 8(1)(d) and (e) and the requirements of paragraphs 5 and 6 of Schedule 1 shall not apply to any activity at an offshore installation carried out for the purposes of the offshore installation.

(a) S.I. 1998/2451
(b) 1954 c. 70, extended by the Mines and Quarries (Tips) Act 1969 (c. 10) and the Mines Managment Act 1971 (c. 20); relevant amending instruments are S.I. 1974/2013, 1976/2063 and 1993/1897
(c) S.I. 1999/2024
(d) S.I. 1995/2038
(e) OJ No. L23, 28.1.00, p.57

Maritime activities

86   Except for Royal Navy ships, DSEAR does not apply to activities involving dangerous substances on ships in Great Britain waters. For example, use of flammable paints and adhesives for maintenance purposes. Similarly when the ship is tied-up in a port or harbour, minor 'running repairs' involving dangerous substances (eg repairs involving flammable adhesives) carried out

solely by the crew under the direction of the ship's master are not covered by DSEAR (except when carried out in a dry dock). In both of these circumstances safety is controlled by maritime legislation produced and enforced by the Maritime and Coastguard Agency.

87   However, when a ship is in port in Great Britain and 'shoreside' workers and the ship's crew work together, eg in dock operations, or in carrying out repairs to the ship, these Regulations may apply. Dock operations, ship construction and work connected to construction or the offshore industry (other than navigation, pollution prevention and other aspects of the operation of the ship, which are subject to international shipping standards) are not considered as 'normal ship-board activities' and are therefore subject to these Regulations.

88   Regulation 3(1) also enables the provisions of regulations 15, 16, 17(4) and 17(5) to be applied in full to water transport and shipping activities where they may be subject to the legislation referred to in those Regulations.

Exclusions from regulations 5(4)(c), 7 and 11

89   Regulation 3(2) lists a number of areas and activities to which regulations: 5(4)(c) (recording information where an explosive atmosphere may occur at the workplace); 7 (places where explosive atmospheres may occur); and regulation 11 (duty of coordination) do not apply. This is because other more specific legislation exists that achieves a corresponding level of safety.

Areas used directly for and during the medical treatment of patients

90   In this regulation 'areas' is limited to the specific areas where medical treatment takes place such as treatment rooms and operating theatres. It does not include, for example, areas in a hospital or surgery where treatment does not take place such as waiting rooms, corridors, boiler rooms, laundries, fitters' workshops or in treatment areas whilst they are undergoing repairs or refurbishment.

The use of gas appliances burning gaseous fuels in accordance with Directive 90/396/EEC - Gas Appliances (Safety) Regulations 1995

91   Appliances not covered by these Regulations are those which burn gaseous fuels for cooking, heating, water heating, refrigeration, lighting and washing with, where appropriate, a normal water temperature not exceeding 105 °C. Appliances specifically designed for use in industrial processes on industrial premises are not excluded. Appliances that heat water to a temperature greater than 105 °C are covered by these Regulations. 'Gaseous fuels' means any fuel which is a gas at a temperature of 15 °C and a pressure of 1 bar (normal atmospheric pressure). 'Use of appliances' does not include installation and maintenance. Regulation 3(2)(b) disapplies from regulations 7 and 11 the use of gas appliances to which the Gas Appliances (Safety) Regulations 1995[43] apply.

Gas fittings

92   The requirements of regulations 5(4)(c), 7 and 11 do not apply to work in domestic premises involving the installation and use of gas fittings as defined in the Gas Safety (Installation and Use) Regulations 1998.[44]

The manufacture, handling, use, storage, and transport of explosives or chemically unstable substances

93   Regulations 5(4)(c), 7 and 11 do not apply to activities involving the manufacture (which includes the storage of raw materials at the manufacturing site where these are to be used for the purpose of manufacture), handling, use and storage of explosives and chemically unstable substances, or to their transport by road, rail, water and air. The safety of activities involving these substances is covered, as appropriate, by other more specific legislation including the Explosive Act 1875[45] and relevant legislation on the carriage or transport of explosives and dangerous goods.

94   For the purpose of these Regulations, 'chemically unstable substances' are substances or preparations which, under conditions likely to occur during the course of a work activity, on its own, or mixed with a combustible material, can, without the need for the involvement of air, undergo a self-sustaining chemical reaction capable of producing heat and/or gas at such a temperature or rate as to present a risk by thermal, blast or fragment projection effects. They include many organic peroxides and various blowing agents of the 'azo' type.

95   There are a small number of cases where specific substances have both the properties of a flammable gas that can form an explosive atmosphere with air and can also explode in the absence of air. Examples include acetylene, methyl acetylene and ethylene oxide. Regulations 5(4)(c), 7 and 11 apply to these substances in relation to the possible formation of explosive atmospheres. The regulations do not apply, however, in relation to their explosive/chemically unstable properties.

Mineral extracting industries

96   Regulations 5(4)(c), 7 and 11 do not apply to activities at mines, quarries or borehole sites insofar as the activities fall within the scope of the legislation referred to in regulation 3(2)(e), (f) and (g) where these are carried out for the specific purpose of the extraction. Nor do they apply to activities at an offshore installation carried out for the purposes of the installation.

97   The requirements for visual or audible warnings (regulations 5(2)(f), (g), (h) and (i), 6(4)(d), 6(5)(b) and (e)) and escape facilities in emergencies (regulations 8(1)(d) and (e)) and appropriate systems of work (paragraph 5 and 6 of Schedule 1) also do not apply to activities at offshore installations because similar requirements exist in other specific offshore legislation.

Use of means of transport

98   The provisions in regulations 5(4)(c), 7 and 11 do not apply means of transport of dangerous goods covered by the following international agreements and the European and domestic legislation that implement them, unless the transport is intended to be used in a potentially explosive atmosphere (the international agreements may have a wider scope than domestic legislation):

(a)   The European Agreement concerning the International Carriage of Dangerous Goods by Road (ADR),[46] implemented in Great Britain through:

-   the Radioactive Materials (Road Transport) Regulations 2002 (RAMRoad);[47]

-   the Classification and Labelling of Explosives Regulations 1983 (CLER);[48]

-   the Packaging of Explosives for Carriage Regulations 1991 (PEC);[49]

-   the Carriage of Explosives by Road Regulations 1996 (CER);[50]

-   the Carriage of Dangerous Goods by Road Regulations 1996 (CDGRoad);[29]

-   the Carriage of Dangerous Goods (Classification, Packaging and Labelling) and Use of Transportable Pressure Receptacles Regulations 1996 (CDGCPL);[51]

-   the Carriage of Dangerous Goods by Road (Driver Training) Regulations 1996 (DTR);[52]

-   the Transport of Dangerous Goods (Safety Advisers) Regulations 1999 (DGSA).[53]

(b)   The European Agreement concerning the International Carriage of Dangerous Goods by Rail (RID),[54] implemented in Great Britain through:

-   the Packaging and Labelling and Carriage of Radioactive Material by Rail Regulations 2002 (RAMRail);[55]

-   the Classification and Labelling of Explosives Regulations 1983 (CLER);[48]

-   the Packaging of Explosives for Carriage Regulations 1991 (PEC);[49]

-   the Carriage of Dangerous Goods (Classification, Packaging and Labelling) and Use of Transportable Pressure Receptacles Regulations 1996 (CDGCPL);[51]

-   the Carriage of Dangerous Goods by Rail Regulations 1996 (CDGRail);[56] and

-   the Transport of Dangerous Goods (Safety Advisers) Regulations 1999 (DGSA).[53]

(c)   The International Civil Aviation Organisation Instructions for the Safe Transport of Dangerous Goods by Air (ICAO)[57] technical instructions are implemented by Air Navigation (Dangerous Goods) Regulations 2002.[58]

(d)   The International Maritime Dangerous Goods Code 2002 (IMDG)[59] code is implemented in Great Britain through the Merchant Shipping (Dangerous Goods and Marine Pollutants) Regulations.[60]

99   If the means of transport covered by the agreements, etc listed above are intended to be used in a potentially explosive atmosphere then they are outside the scope of the disapplication and are subject to regulations 5(4)(c), 7 and 11.

100 It is possible that loading/unloading operations may take place in an area where there is a potentially explosive atmosphere and, if this is the case, the requirements of regulations 5(4)(c), 7 and 11 will apply to the means of transport. However, this does not include situations where an explosive atmosphere is likely to occur solely as a result of a loading/unloading operation itself. For example, the disapplication would apply to a road tanker transporting petrol, where the loading/unloading site is not initially considered to have a potentially explosive atmosphere because of its location with respect to the storage facility.

101 The more specific provisions of the legislation on the transport of dangerous goods apply as normal to ensure safety during transport, loading and unloading.

102 The transport of dangerous goods outside the scope of international agreements etc is not covered by the disapplication and is fully subject to regulations 5(4)(c), 7 and 11. Generally, this includes vehicles that do not leave the employer's premises, such as fork lift trucks, etc working in potentially explosive atmospheres.

Regulation 4

Duties under these Regulations

(1)   Where a duty is placed by these Regulations on an employer in respect of his employees, he shall, so far as is reasonably practicable, be under a like duty in respect of any other person, whether at work or not, who may be affected by the work carried on by the employer, except that -

(a)   the duties of the employer under regulations 6(5)(f) and 7(5) (which relate, respectively, to the provision of suitable personal protective equipment and the provision of appropriate work clothing) shall not extend to persons who are not his employees; and

(b)   the duties of the employer under regulations 8 and 9 (which relate, respectively, to dealing with accidents and to provision of information, instruction and training) shall not extend to persons who are not his employees, unless those persons are at the workplace where the work is being carried on and subject to the following, namely, that, in relation to the application of regulation 9 to such persons, regulation 9 shall apply to the extent that is required by the nature and the degree of the risk.

(2)   These Regulations shall apply to a self-employed person as they apply to an employer and an employee and as if that self-employed person were both an employer and employee.

103 These Regulations place specific duties on employers to assess and control the risks from dangerous substances. For the purposes of these Regulations, employers include contractors, sub-contractors and self-employed people. The duties under these Regulations apply to a self-employed person as if he were both an employer and an employee.

104 In addition to their own employees, employers are required to take account of the risks to people who are not employed by them but who may be at risk from the use or presence of dangerous substances at the workplace. This includes employees working for other employers, visitors to the site, members of the public, living or working nearby etc.

105 However, for the purposes of regulation 8 (arrangements to deal with accidents, incidents and emergencies) and regulation 9 (information, instruction and training), employers only have duties to people other than their employees when those people are on their premises. In addition, employers are not required to provide people other than their employees with appropriate personal protective equipment or work clothing. In relation to non-employees, information, instruction and training need only be provided to the extent required by the level and type of risk.

106 Where employees of one employer work at another employer's premises, both employers have duties under the Regulations. Each employer has duties to their own and the other employer's employees. The employers should co-operate and collaborate to ensure that all the duties imposed by these Regulations are fulfilled. Arrangements for this may need to be agreed between them, but each employer will need to satisfy himself that any arrangements adopted are adequate.

107 Where, after 30 June 2003, two or more employers share the same workplace where an explosive atmosphere may occur, regulation 11 places a duty on the employer responsible to co-ordinate the implementation of any explosion protection measures required by these Regulations.

Risk assessment

(1)   Where a dangerous substance is or is liable to be present at the workplace, the employer shall make a suitable and sufficient assessment of the risks to his employees which arise from that substance.

(2)   The risk assessment shall include consideration of -

(a)   the hazardous properties of the substance;

(b)   information on safety provided by the supplier, including information contained in any relevant safety data sheet;

(c)   the circumstances of the work including -

> *(i)   the work processes and substances used and their possible interactions;*
>
> *(ii)   the amount of the substance involved;*
>
> *(iii)   where the work will involve more than one dangerous substance, the risk presented by such substances in combination; and*
>
> *(iv)   the arrangements for the safe handling, storage and transport of dangerous substances and of waste containing dangerous substances;*

(d)   activities, such as maintenance, where there is the potential for a high level of risk;

(e)   the effect of measures which have been or will be taken pursuant to these Regulations;

(f)   the likelihood that an explosive atmosphere will occur and its persistence;

(g)   the likelihood that ignition sources, including electrostatic discharges, will be present and become active and effective;

(h)   the scale of the anticipated effects of a fire or an explosion;

(i)   any places which are or can be connected via openings to places in which explosive atmospheres may occur; and

(j)   such additional safety information as the employer may need in order to complete the risk assessment.

(3)   The risk assessment shall be reviewed by the employer regularly so as to keep it up to date and particularly if -

(a)   there is reason to suspect that the risk assessment is no longer valid; or

(b)   there has been a significant change in the matters to which the risk assessment relates including when the workplace, work processes, or organisation of the work undergoes significant changes, extensions or conversions;

and where, as a result of the review, changes to the risk assessment are required, those changes shall be made.

(4)   Where the employer employs five or more employees, the employer shall record the significant findings of the risk assessment as soon as is practicable after that assessment is made, including in particular -

(a)   the measures which have been or will be taken by him pursuant to these Regulations;

(b)   sufficient information to show that the workplace and work processes are designed, operated and maintained with due regard for safety and that, in accordance with the Provision and Use of Work Equipment Regulations 1998[a], adequate arrangements have been made for the safe use of work equipment; and

(c)   where an explosive atmosphere may occur at the workplace and subject to the transitional provisions in regulation 17(1) to (3), sufficient information to show -

(i)   those places which have been classified into zones pursuant to regulation 7(1);

(ii)   equipment which is required for, or helps to ensure, the safe operation of equipment located in places classified as hazardous pursuant to regulation 7(1);

(iii)   that any verification of overall explosion safety required by regulation 7(4) has been carried out; and

(iv)   the aim of any coordination required by regulation 11 and the measures and procedures for implementing it.

(5)   No new work activity involving a dangerous substance shall commence unless -

(a)   an assessment has been made; and

(b)   the measures required by these Regulations have been implemented.

(a) S.I. 1998/2306, amended by S.I. 1999/860 and 1999/2001

Risk assessment

108 Regulation 5 requires employers to assess the risks to workers (and any others who may be affected by their work or business) which may arise because of the presence of dangerous substances at the workplace.

109 The assessment is carried out to identify safety risks arising out of, or in connection with, work or the conduct of an employer's undertaking that relate to dangerous substances. It should identify how those risks arise and how they impact on those affected. An assessment must be undertaken before any new work activity involving dangerous substances begins.

110 The risk assessment should take into account the effects of measures, which have been or will be taken to eliminate or control risks. This includes consideration of general fire precautions such as means of detection and giving warning in case of fire.

111 The requirement to assess the risks from dangerous substances should not be considered in isolation. It should be carried out as part of the overall risk assessment required by regulation 3 of the MHSW Regulations 1999,[11] rather than as a separate exercise.

112 The risk assessment process should take into account the views of employees and their representatives (such as safety and trade union representatives) who will have practical knowledge to contribute. It should also include management input.

113 If the dangerous substances present are also a risk to the health of employees and others (ie they are toxic, carcinogenic, etc), employers will also need to assess health risks as required by the COSHH Regulations 2002.[14]

114 The risk assessment required by regulation 5 is an identification and careful examination of the dangerous substances present in the workplace and how fire, explosion and similar events might harm employees and any other people affected by the work concerned. Its purpose is to enable employers to decide what they need to do to eliminate or reduce the risks from dangerous substances, so far as is reasonably practicable. Employers should ensure that whoever carries out the assessment should be competent to do so.

115 The risk assessment required by DSEAR should not be carried out in isolation from that required by the MHSW Regulations.[11] Employers should take into account all risks when carrying out an assessment. The assessment requirement in DSEAR focuses on the risks and issues that should be considered when assessing activities that involve the presence and/or use of dangerous substances.

116 The assessment (including the recording of significant findings) enables employers to demonstrate to themselves, and to others who may have an interest, eg inspectors, employees' representatives (including safety and trade union representatives) etc, that they have followed a structured and thorough approach in considering the risks to the safety of employees and the control measures that are needed.

117 Further information on how to undertake a suitable and sufficient risk assessment is provided in HSE's Approved Code of Practice and Guidance[61] to the MHSW Regulations.[11]

118 The risk assessment could, where appropriate, be completed alongside goal-orientated risk assessments, such as the BS IEC 61508[62] or BS IEC 61511[63] sector standards used by process industry, providing that risks from fire, explosion and other events arising from dangerous substances are addressed, including the requirements specified by DSEAR.

Factors to consider when carrying out a risk assessment

119 Employers will need to consider a number of factors when assessing risks from dangerous substances. Regulation 5(2) sets out a number of factors (relevant to dangerous substances) which should be taken into account when undertaking a risk assessment. The following paragraphs provide further guidance on these factors.

The hazardous properties of a substance

120 Employers will need to identify any dangerous substances that may be present at the workplace and the hazards they present (eg their flammable or explosive properties).

121 This includes substances which are:

(a) brought into the workplace and handled, stored and used for processing;

(b) produced or given off (eg as fumes, vapour, dust etc) by a process or activity, or as a result of an incident or accident;

(c) used for, or arise from maintenance, cleaning, and repair work; or

(d) produced as a by product of any work or process (eg waste, residues, scrap materials etc);

(e) naturally occurring in the workplace (eg methane may be present in tunnelling and mining operations.

122 Careful thought is needed when considering what dangerous substances may be present in the workplace. Some substances, such as petrol and liquefied petroleum gas, are obviously hazardous to safety. However, other substances might be hazardous only under certain conditions, such as flour dust (which could form an explosive atmosphere) or high flashpoint liquids such as diesel fuel (which could be raised above their flashpoint temperature by work activities and present a fire or explosion risk).

Information on safety provided by the supplier of a dangerous substance

123 Useful information on the properties and hazards of dangerous substances may be provided by suppliers eg in safety data sheets. This could include details such as flashpoints or explosive or chemical properties. Other information could relate to safe methods of using, storing and handling the substances.

The circumstances of the work

124 This includes careful consideration of: the work processes as defined in regulation 2(1) and the substances used; the amounts of those substances present; and arrangements for their handling, storage and transportation. Thought should also be given to the risks presented by substances in combination.

125 Employers need to consider potential hazards arising from equipment, etc used in processing or handling dangerous substances. This includes equipment that may be brought into an area where dangerous substances are present. Employers should also look at the process operations themselves to ensure that they are carried out in a safe manner.

126 In particular, consideration should be given to:

(a) the potential for dangerous substances to be released (either intentionally or unintentionally) from plant/equipment, or during handling;

(b) the potential for explosive atmospheres to form;

(c) the likelihood of unintentional ignition sources from equipment, etc; and

(d) the effectiveness of the plant/equipment to mitigate the effects of an incident.

127 Employers should also consider whether the equipment is designed and installed to appropriate standards and whether it is regularly inspected and maintained.

128 Risks will vary depending on the quantities of dangerous substances present and may be greater where large quantities of a substance are involved.

129 Most processes and operations will use more than one dangerous substance and it is important to consider how these could react or behave together to give rise to a hazardous situation. For example:

(a) where substances are used together in a chemical process it will be necessary to carry out a chemical reaction hazard assessment so as to avoid any adverse conditions that could give rise to hazardous heat and pressure effects;

(b) where different substances are stored, incompatible materials, such as self-reactive substances and flammable liquids, should not be kept together;

(c) where substances with different properties are processed together the fire properties of any resulting mixture will be different from the individual components. It will be necessary to ascertain the properties of the mixture to ensure, for example, any electrical equipment is suitable and any explosion relief provided is appropriate;

(d) oxygen and other oxidising agents make most flammable substances easier to ignite, burn faster and become more difficult to extinguish. Many materials, which are not classified as dangerous substances, will become dangerous in the presence of pure oxygen or an oxidising agent. Where oxygen or other oxidising agents are used near to dangerous substances or combustible materials, the assessment will need to take into account the enhanced fire properties.

130 Employers should take account of the work activities involving dangerous substances when assessing risk. This could include such activities as:

(a) loading and unloading operations (and the frequency of delivery/dispatch of dangerous substances);

(b) dispensing and decanting activities;

(c) movement of dangerous substances around the site; and

(d) how spillages and leaks are dealt with.

Particular activities, which may present a high level of risk

131 In addition to 'normal' activities such as storage or manufacturing processes, some activities, such as maintenance and repair, may require specific procedures, which expose workers to risks from dangerous substances. This could include, for example, dismantling equipment containing dangerous substances. Such activities will need to be considered and included in the risk assessment. See the activity specific DSEAR ACOPs for *Design of plant, equipment and workplaces*[2] and *Safe maintenance, repair and cleaning procedures*[5] for further information.

The effect of any measures already in place or taken as a result of DSEAR

132 Employers should take into account the effect of any measures already in place, or measures specified by DSEAR, which will be put in place to prevent or control risks. Further information on control and other preventive measures can be found in regulations 6 to 11.

The likely presence of explosive atmospheres and the need for hazardous area classification

133 Gases, vapours, mists and dusts can give rise to explosive atmospheres. Hazardous area classification, as required by regulation 7, is intended to identify places where, because of the potential for an explosive atmosphere, controls over sources of ignition are required. The results of the classification are then used to control the equipment that may be used, or the work activities that may be carried out, in these areas so as to prevent ignition.

134 Employers should carry out hazardous area classification as an integral part of the risk assessment so as to identify places where controls over ignition sources are needed and those places where they are not. Schedule 2 sets out definitions of the zones to be used when classifying hazardous areas. These definitions recognise that, in many cases, explosive atmospheres will not be present constantly, and that the chance of a fire or explosion depends on the likelihood of an explosive atmosphere occurring at the same time as an ignition source becomes active.

135 Schedule 2 defines a place where an explosive atmosphere may occur in such quantities as to require special precautions to protect the health and safety of workers as hazardous. A place where an explosive atmosphere is not expected to occur in such quantities as to require such special precautions is deemed to be non-hazardous. 'Special precautions' should be taken to mean precautions to control potential ignition sources within a hazardous area, in particular in relation to the construction, installation and use of equipment.

136 The term 'not expected to occur in such quantities' means that employers should consider the likelihood of releases of explosive atmospheres as well as the potential quantity of such releases when considering area classification. So if a release is extremely unlikely to occur and/or if the quantities released are small, it may not be necessary to classify the area as hazardous.

- the Classification and Labelling of Explosives Regulations 1983 (CLER);[48]

- the Packaging of Explosives for Carriage Regulations 1991 (PEC);[49]

- the Carriage of Explosives by Road Regulations 1996 (CER);[50]

- the Carriage of Dangerous Goods by Road Regulations 1996 (CDGRoad);[29]

- the Carriage of Dangerous Goods (Classification, Packaging and Labelling) and Use of Transportable Pressure Receptacles Regulations 1996 (CDGCPL);[51]

- the Carriage of Dangerous Goods by Road (Driver Training) Regulations 1996 (DTR);[52]

- the Transport of Dangerous Goods (Safety Advisers) Regulations 1999 (DGSA).[53]

(b) The European Agreement concerning the International Carriage of Dangerous Goods by Rail (RID),[54] implemented in Great Britain through:

- the Packaging and Labelling and Carriage of Radioactive Material by Rail Regulations 2002 (RAMRail);[55]

- the Classification and Labelling of Explosives Regulations 1983 (CLER);[48]

- the Packaging of Explosives for Carriage Regulations 1991 (PEC);[49]

- the Carriage of Dangerous Goods (Classification, Packaging and Labelling) and Use of Transportable Pressure Receptacles Regulations 1996 (CDGCPL);[51]

- the Carriage of Dangerous Goods by Rail Regulations 1996 (CDGRail);[56] and

- the Transport of Dangerous Goods (Safety Advisers) Regulations 1999 (DGSA).[53]

(c) The International Civil Aviation Organisation Instructions for the Safe Transport of Dangerous Goods by Air (ICAO)[57] technical instructions are implemented by Air Navigation (Dangerous Goods) Regulations 2002.[58]

(d) The International Maritime Dangerous Goods Code 2002 (IMDG)[59] code is implemented in Great Britain through the Merchant Shipping (Dangerous Goods and Marine Pollutants) Regulations.[60]

99   If the means of transport covered by the agreements, etc listed above are intended to be used in a potentially explosive atmosphere then they are outside the scope of the disapplication and are subject to regulations 5(4)(c), 7 and 11.

point of any flammable liquid, and whether any flammable gas or vapour that may be evolved is lighter or heavier than air. For dusts, information on particle size and density will be needed, once it has been shown that a particular dust can form an explosive atmosphere. Often, relevant information is contained on a safety data sheet provided with the product.

Size of release

143 Some potential sources of release may be so small that there is no need to specify a zoned area. This will be the case if the consequence of an ignition following a release is unlikely to cause danger to people in the vicinity. However, in the wrong circumstances ignition of quite small quantities of flammable gas/vapour mixed with air can cause danger to anyone in the immediate vicinity. Where this is the case, as in a relatively confined location from which rapid escape would be difficult, area classification may be needed even where quite small quantities of a dangerous substance are present.

144 The size of any potential release of dangerous substances is in part related to the amount of dangerous substances present. Industry specific codes have been published by a variety of organisations to provide guidance on the quantities of various dangerous substances that can be stored. For example, the *Code of practice on storage of full and empty LPG cylinders and cartridges*[64] produced by the Liquefied Petroleum Gas Association (LPGA).

Temperatures and pressures

145 Additional information relating to the process rather than the substance should also be taken into account, including the temperatures and pressures used in the facility, as this will influence the nature and extent of any release of dangerous substances, and hence the extent of any subsequent hazardous areas. Some substances do not form explosive atmospheres unless they are heated, and some liquids if released under pressure will form a fine mist that can explode even if there is insufficient vapour.

Ventilation

146 Ventilation, either natural, or mechanically induced (eg by a fan), can both dilute sources of release, and remove dangerous substances from an enclosed area. Consequently there is a close link between the ventilation at any given location, and the classification and extent of a zone around a potential source of release. Well-designed ventilation may prevent the need for any zoned area around a source of release, or reduce it so it has a negligible extent.

Extent of zones

147 The assessment needs to identify areas within the workplace that are connected to places where an explosive atmosphere may occur. This will provide information on any areas away from the source of the hazard to which an explosive atmosphere may spread, for example through ducts. Such areas should be included in the classification system for places where explosive atmospheres may occur. An approach to assessing this risk is described in BS EN 60079/10.[65] One technique for minimising this risk is described in BS EN 50016[66] on pressurisation of enclosures containing electrical equipment.

Other considerations

148 When considering the possible formation of potentially explosive atmospheres, it is important to consider all dangerous substances that may be

present at the workplace, including waste products, residues, materials used for cleaning or maintenance, and any used only as a fuel. Also some combinations of dangerous substances may react together, forming an ignition source, or in combination may form an explosive atmosphere, where singly this does not occur. Such possibilities should be considered in the risk assessment.

149 Some repeated activities such as refuelling cars, or loading and unloading tankers intended for use on the public roads, involve the introduction of potential sources of ignition into an area where a spill is possible, and which would meet the description of a hazardous area. In these circumstances, safety can be achieved by isolating power sources (eg turning off engines, etc) while a transfer is taking place, and making suitable checks before and after a transfer, before moving a vehicle into or out of a hazardous area. The risk assessment made under regulation 5 should consider the controls necessary.

150 Some activities, such as maintenance, may incur risks not covered by the normal area classification of the area where the activity is taking place, for instance the introduction of sources of ignition into a hazardous area. Sometimes the dangerous substance can be removed before the maintenance work activity starts. Sometimes, special control measures can be taken to prevent the release of any dangerous substance during the work. In such cases the additional risks associated with the activity should be assessed before work starts.

Relationship between fires and explosions

151 In many cases where an explosive atmosphere can form, any ignition will cause a fire rather than an explosion. Both fire and explosion cause dangers to workers, and in many cases the precautions required to prevent an ignition are the same. The overall package of precautions required will depend on the possible consequences of a fire or explosion.

152 Many factors influence the risks from a fire involving dangerous substances. In particular, employers should consider whether a fire could lead to an explosion, how fast a fire might grow, what other materials might be rapidly evolved, any dangers from smoke and toxic gases given off, and whether those in the vicinity would be able to escape.

The presence of ignition sources and how likely it is for them to give rise to a fire or explosion

153 Flammable substances (particularly when in the form of an explosive atmosphere) are readily ignited. It is important to identify where ignition sources (including electrostatic discharges) could be present. An ignition source is a release of energy, often of short duration and localised, which can ignite dangerous substances in the presence of air. The assessment should therefore identify places at the workplace where ignition sources may arise in the presence of dangerous substances and cause a fire, explosion or similar energetic event.

154 All potential sources of ignition in these areas should be taken into account. Many sources of ignition are easy to identify, such as naked flames, but others may be less obvious: such as sparks caused by friction in mechanical equipment; the operation of electrical equipment; hot surfaces; and electrostatic discharges from an individual.

155 The assessment should address how likely it is that the particular ignition source will ignite the dangerous substance present. This part of the assessment

will need to take into account the information obtained from the assessment of the hazardous properties of the substance and information on safety provided by the supplier. The reference to 'active' in this regulation means that potential sources of ignition are present; for static electricity this means that a static charge is present. The reference to 'effective' means that the energy of the potential source of ignition is sufficient to cause an ignition of the particular dangerous substance present. In the case of static electricity it means that the level of charge is sufficiently high to ignite the substance present.

The scale of the anticipated physical effects and the extent of harm arising from the fire, explosion or similar event

156　The scale of effects and the extent of harm will depend on the amount of heat radiated and the size of any forces created either directly or indirectly from an incident. These in turn will depend on the amounts of material involved, how quickly they can be consumed, how the incident could escalate and whether conditions exist or could develop to cause a fire, explosion, or similar event.

157　Where an explosion is likely the scale of the effects will depend on the material; the size of the potential explosive atmosphere; the strength and shape of the containment; and whether the internal configuration or any obstructions will accelerate the burning rates. Consideration of these factors will allow an assessment of who will be affected by an accident, and to what extent, and what mitigation measures will be required.

Places which are or can be connected via openings to places in which explosive atmospheres may occur

158　The assessment needs to identify areas within the workplace that are connected to places where an explosive atmosphere may occur. This will provide information on any areas away from the source of the hazard to which an explosive atmosphere may spread, for example through ducts. Such areas should be included in the classification system for places where explosive atmospheres may occur set out in regulation 7 and Schedule 2.

159　Openings between rooms within a building also provide a route for the spread of any release of flammable material that is released in an incident, and also a route for the effects of flames, burning particles or pressure waves to spread to other parts of a building or plant. These possibilities should be considered in any risk assessment so that the appropriate preventive, control and other measures required by the Regulations can be determined.

Any additional information that may help in the development of the risk assessment

160　This additional information could include:

(a)　the skills, knowledge and experience of employees and their representatives;

(b)　the training and supervision of employees;

(c)　activities in adjacent areas or on adjacent premises, particularly where this could present an ignition risk; and

(d)　possible misuse of dangerous substances, for example, to burn waste.

161 Further information on the assessment of risk for a variety of activities and circumstances can be found in the activity specific ACOPs for DSEAR on *Design of plant, equipment and workplaces,*[2] *Storage of dangerous substances,*[3] *Control and mitigation measures,*[4] and *Safe maintenance, repair and cleaning procedures.*[5]

Assessing the overall risk

162 When carrying out a suitable and sufficient risk assessment it is important that employers also assess the overall risk presented by dangerous substances as well as assessing each factor separately.

Fire safety issues

163 Employers' risk assessments (and the record of the assessment where one is required) will also need to take account of any general fire precautions such as means of escape. An explanation of how to comply with the law relating to fire issues and how to carry out a fire risk assessment can be found in the guide *Fire safety. An employer's guide.*[67]

164 General fire precautions include:

(a) means of detection and giving warning in case of fire;

(b) provision of means of escape;

(c) means of fighting fire; and

(d) the training of staff in fire safety.

165 In most workplaces, the local fire authority enforces the fire precautions legislation and they will also enforce those parts of DSEAR which cover general fire precautions required for the safety of people in case of fire. In so far as they relate to general fire precautions, regulations 1-6, 8, 9 and 11 of DSEAR are made part of the 'workplace fire precautions legislation'.

166 Other requirements for preventing and controlling fires under these Regulations - such as measures to prevent leaks of dangerous substances and avoid sources of ignition, will be enforced by HSE or the local authority, depending on the activity in the premises.

Identifying who might be harmed and to what extent

167 Employers should identify those people who may be harmed by the dangerous substances present. They should also consider the ways in which, and the extent to which, people may be put at risk. Different groups of workers could be put at risk to varying degrees, eg office staff, production workers, night cleaners, etc.

168 Employers should also be aware of the need to consider particular groups of employees who may be at increased risk because of lack of awareness of the risks from dangerous substances; eg inexperienced trainees and young people under 18.

169 Non-employees should also be taken account of in the risk assessment. This includes employees of another employer working in the workplace and members of the public and other visitors, both on and off-site.

170 It is important to remember that substances with flammable or explosive properties have the potential to harm people off-site as well as those at the workplace itself.

Reviewing and revising the risk assessment

171 Risk assessment should not be a once-and-for-all activity. The nature of dangerous substances and the way in which they are used may change or new work processes or equipment may be introduced. Regulation 5(3) requires employers to review and if necessary modify the risk assessment.

172 Employers should plan to review their risk assessment at regular intervals. The time between reviews depends on the nature of the risks presented by the dangerous substances and the degree of change likely in the work activity. The risk assessment should also be reviewed if developments suggest that it may no longer be valid.

173 Changes in the workplace which should require a risk assessment to be reviewed include:

(a) changes to the substances used;

(b) replacement or modification to the plant and/or equipment used;

(c) changes in processes or methods of work which could effect the nature of hazards and risks; and

(d) changes in the workforce - such as reductions in numbers or experience of employees involved in a work activity.

174 Employers should review their risk assessment following an accident or dangerous occurrence.

175 Adverse events such as accidents or dangerous incidents may take place even if a suitable and sufficient risk assessment has been made and appropriate preventive and protective measures taken. Such events should be a trigger for reviewing the original assessment.

176 When reviewing the risk assessment employers should take the opportunity to reconsider their control and or mitigation measures including:

(a) whether it is now practical to replace the substance or process with one which either eliminates or reduces the risk - this may be possible due to changes in technology or economic costs since the risk assessment was originally carried out or last reviewed; and

(b) a re-examination of the control/mitigation measures in place to see if they can be improved.

177 Employers must make changes to their control measures where the review of a risk assessment indicates that this is required. The record of significant findings should also be revised as necessary.

Recording the significant findings of the risk assessment

178   All employers must carry out a risk assessment but a record of the significant findings is only required where they employ five or more employees. Although employers with fewer than five employees are exempt from this recording requirement, they are strongly advised to record the significant findings of their assessment as a matter of good practice. This includes the preventive measures taken to control risk in accordance with these Regulations. Additional information must be recorded where the risk assessment shows that an explosive atmosphere may occur.

When to record

179   The employer should record the significant findings as soon as is practicable after the assessment is made. In some circumstances, not all the significant findings will have been determined at the same time: some may be awaiting further information before they can be resolved and it will not be possible to record these until then. In these situations, the employer should complete or update the findings as soon as the information becomes available. However, the employer must ensure that, while waiting for information to confirm the conclusions drawn from the assessment, a cautious approach is adopted with regard to eliminating or reducing risks from dangerous substances to ensure employees' safety: or in circumstances where there is a pilot operation which must be run for a period before being assessed completely.

What to record

180   The record should represent an effective statement of the hazards and risks from dangerous substances which lead employers to take the relevant actions to protect safety. Where appropriate it should be linked to other health and safety records or documents, particularly the record of risk assessment made under the MHSW Regulations,[11] COSHH,[14] and the written health and safety policy statement required by section 2(3) of the HSW Act.[8] It may be possible to combine these documents into one health and safety management document.

181   The record may be in writing or recorded by other means (eg electronically). It should be readily retrievable for use by management in reviews, for safety representatives or other employee representatives, and visiting inspectors. It can refer to other documents and records describing procedures and safeguards.

182   The amount of information that should be recorded depends on the level of risks present in the workplace. In cases where a dangerous substance poses little or no risk (for example many of the substances often found in an office environment), employers may only need to record:

(a)   the identity of the dangerous substances present and the risks they present;

(b)   the measures taken under DSEAR; and

(c)   if appropriate, because of the safeguards taken, an explanatory statement that a further detailed assessment is unnecessary.

183 However, where dangerous substances in the workplace present a greater risk, the assessment record should be more comprehensive. It should include:

(a) the preventive measures in place to control the risks, including those required by regulation 6 (this can include reference to measures described more fully in other documents);

(b) enough information to demonstrate that the workplace and work processes are designed, operated and maintained with due regard to safety;

(c) that adequate arrangements have been made for the safe use of work equipment, in accordance with PUWER;[20]

(d) where explosive atmospheres may be present, and subject to the transitional provisions in regulations 17(1) to (3), information on the zoning of hazardous areas, the equipment used, any co-ordination between employers that may be necessary, and any verification of overall explosion safety.

Information to be recorded when explosive atmospheres may be present

Information on the workplace and work equipment

184 The record should demonstrate that the workplace and work processes are safe for work with dangerous substances, taking into account the properties of the dangerous substances, the equipment provided and the way this will be used. In particular the record may need to consider plant and machinery that will be used, engineering controls and protective systems that are provided, and whether the materials of construction are compatible with the dangerous substances.

185 For the workplace this should show, for example, that its design allows for a process to be carried out safely such as by the provision of a storage area for dangerous substances, or to allow sufficient space to segregate incompatible substances.

186 For work equipment, the record should show that equipment is suitable for work with the dangerous substance(s) involved. For equipment intended for use in an explosive atmosphere one way to do this is by reference to the classification of hazardous places into zones under regulation 7(1), and evidence of the selection of a suitable category of equipment in accordance with the manufacturer's or supplier's instructions.

187 The record should show that the workplace and work equipment are maintained in a safe state and, where necessary, that arrangements exist for periodic maintenance, testing and other checks or inspections. This may be shown through reference to a maintenance log.

188 In many cases much of the information required by regulation 5(4) will be considered under the employer's duties set out in PUWER.[20] Where a record has been made to demonstrate compliance with PUWER this record may also be suitable to demonstrate compliance with DSEAR provided that it contains sufficient information.

Hazardous places and zones

189 Where an explosive atmosphere may occur at the workplace, sufficient information should be recorded to show those places that have been classified as hazardous in accordance with regulation 7(1) and Schedule 2, and the zones used. Hazard area classification drawings would be suitable for this purpose.

190 The record should also identify any equipment which is required for, or helps to ensure, the safe operation of equipment located in zoned areas.

191 The requirement for area classification under regulation 7 applies to a workplace when normal activities are taking place. When special precautions are required eg to allow short-term maintenance or repair (as described in the ACOP on *Safe maintenance, repair and cleaning procedures*[5]), there is no requirement to draw up a revised area classification plan but there is still a requirement to risk assess the short-term conditions.

Coordination measures

192 The record should demonstrate the purpose of the coordination measures required by regulation 11. For example, the aim could be to alert employees of another employer to the presence of hazardous substances or places, or to facilitate emergency arrangements in the event of an accident. The record should also show the arrangements the employer has in place to achieve the aims. This is likely to require reference, for example, to instructions given to other employers or their employees. It will also include information for contractors when they first start on site, including a specification of the work to be done, and arrangements for supervision, and handover procedures for particular items of plant or parts of the premises.

Consulting with employees and their representatives

193 Employers should involve employees and/or their representatives in the risk assessment process, as they will often be in a good position to know what happens in practice during a work activity.

194 Employers should make the significant findings of risk assessments available to employees and their representatives. This will help to explain what the risks are and how the control/mitigation measures are designed to protect their safety. It will also help employees to understand and use the safeguards that employers introduce. Further guidance is given under regulation 9.

Model risk assessments

195 Employers who control a number of similar workplaces containing similar activities may produce a 'model' risk assessment reflecting the core hazards and risks associated with these activities. Trade associations, employers' bodies or other organisations concerned with a particular activity, may also develop 'model' assessments. Such model assessments may be applied by employers or managers at each workplace, but only if they:

(a) satisfy themselves that the model assessment is appropriate to their type of work; and

(b) adapt the model to the detail of their own actual work situations, including any extension necessary to cover hazards and risks not referred to in the model.

Elimination or reduction of risks from dangerous substances

(1) Every employer shall ensure that risk is either eliminated or reduced so far as is reasonably practicable.

(2) In complying with his duty under paragraph (1), substitution shall by preference be undertaken, whereby the employer shall avoid, so far as is reasonably practicable, the presence or use of a dangerous substance at the workplace by replacing it with a substance or process which either eliminates or reduces the risk.

(3) Where it is not reasonably practicable to eliminate risk pursuant to paragraphs (1) and (2), the employer shall, so far as is reasonably practicable, apply measures, consistent with the risk assessment and appropriate to the nature of the activity or operation -

(a) to control risks, including the measures specified in paragraph (4); and

(b) to mitigate the detrimental effects of a fire or explosion or the other harmful physical effects arising from dangerous substances, including the measures specified in paragraph (5).

(4) The following measures are, in order of priority, those specified for the purposes of paragraph (3)(a) -

(a) the reduction of the quantity of dangerous substances to a minimum;

(b) the avoidance or minimising of the release of a dangerous substance;

(c) the control of the release of a dangerous substance at source;

(d) the prevention of the formation of an explosive atmosphere, including the application of appropriate ventilation;

(e) ensuring that any release of a dangerous substance which may give rise to risk is suitably collected, safely contained, removed to a safe place, or otherwise rendered safe, as appropriate;

(f) the avoidance of -

(i) ignition sources including electrostatic discharges; and

(ii) adverse conditions which could cause dangerous substances to give rise to harmful physical effects; and

(g) the segregation of incompatible dangerous substances.

(5) The following measures are those specified for the purposes of paragraph (3)(b) -

(a) the reduction to a minimum of the number of employees exposed;

(b) the avoidance of the propagation of fires or explosions;

(c) the provision of explosion pressure relief arrangements;

(d) the provision of explosion suppression equipment;

(e)   the provision of plant which is constructed so as to withstand the pressure likely to be produced by an explosion; and

(f)   the provision of suitable personal protective equipment.

(6)   The employer shall arrange for the safe handling, storage and transport of dangerous substances and waste containing dangerous substances.

(7)   The employer shall ensure that any conditions necessary pursuant to these Regulations for ensuring the elimination or reduction of risk are maintained.

(8)   The employer shall, so far as is reasonably practicable, take the general safety measures specified in Schedule 1, subject to those measures being consistent with the risk assessment and appropriate to the nature of the activity or operation.

Overall framework

196   Regulation 6(1) requires employers to ensure that the risks to employees (and others who may be at risk) are eliminated or reduced so far as is reasonably practicable.

So far as is reasonably practicable

197   The term 'so far as is reasonably practicable' has been interpreted by the courts as allowing economic considerations as well as, for example, time or trouble, to be taken into account as factors to be set against the risk: if there is gross disproportion between those factors and the risk, the risk being insignificant in relation to the sacrifice (eg money, time or trouble), then a duty holder can say that taking of measures in compliance with a duty would not be reasonably practicable. So, in a particular case, it may be reasonably practicable to take measures up to a certain point, but thereafter it becomes grossly disproportionate to take further measures.

Substitution

198   Regulation 6(2) requires that preference be first given to substituting the dangerous substance(s) with a different substance or substituting a new or modified work process so as to eliminate or reduce the risk.

199   Substitution to eliminate risks is the best solution but in practice it is difficult to achieve. It is likely that it will be more practicable to replace the dangerous substance with one that is less hazardous (eg by replacing a low-flashpoint solvent with a high-flashpoint one).

200   An alternative is to design the process so that it is less dangerous. This might include, for example, changing from a batch production to a continuous production process; or changing the manner or sequence in which the dangerous substance is added. However, care must be taken when carrying out these steps to ensure that no other new safety or health risks are created or increased, which then outweigh the improvements implemented as a result of DSEAR.

201   In many cases, for example, where the dangerous substances handled or stored is for use as a fuel it will not be possible to replace that substance with a substitute.

202   If the risk cannot be eliminated by substitution, then the regulation requires that control and mitigation measures (consistent with the risk assessment and appropriate to the nature of the activity or operation) are taken to reduce risk so far as is reasonably practicable.

203 The employer will need to consider a number of factors when considering if substitution is possible. Some of these are listed below. The ultimate decision should be based on a balance of any new health or safety risks, potential benefits, costs, effectiveness and ease of control of the new substance or process with the hazards to safety currently posed.

204 Employers should follow a logical sequence of steps when deciding whether it is possible to use alternative substances or work processes:

(a)   identify possible alternatives;

(b)   evaluate and compare them; and

(c)   consider risks, benefits, costs, and effectiveness.

205 There are many factors to be taken into account when considering substitution: whether the nature of the work activity allows for substitution (eg it would not be possible to use an alternative to petrol at a retail filling station). These include:

(a)   the physical/chemical properties of substances and their potential effects on safety;

(b)   whether the substitute substance or process poses a greater or lesser hazard to safety;

(c)   whether the substitute substance poses a lesser hazard to safety but a greater hazard to health, eg is it toxic?;

(d)   the physical form of the substance: how easy it is to control and whether a less hazardous and more easily controlled form of the same substance is available;

(e)   whether the substitute substance can do the job as effectively without affecting the process or the quality of the finished product;

(f)   any waste that may be produced and how easily this can be controlled and disposed of;

(g)   costs and whether the substitute substance or process would be economical to use (but note guidance in paragraph 197 on 'so far as is reasonably practicable'; and

(h)   whether an alternative substance will be available in the longer term or is being phased out under domestic or international regulatory initiatives.

206 To identify possible alternative substances or work processes, employers should consult a wide variety of sources of information, eg manufacturers and suppliers, trade associations, HSE inspectors, Government departments such as the Department of Trade and Industry and the Department for Transport.

207 HSE inspectors and local authority environmental health officers, who visit workplaces where hazardous substances are used, will ask employers what efforts they have made to find non-hazardous or less hazardous substitutes for dangerous substances or what efforts they have made to change or modify the work process to eliminate or reduce risks; and to provide some evidence of their enquiries. Employers are advised to keep a record of the alternative substances and work processes that they have considered and a brief explanation of the reasons why, if appropriate, they have been rejected.

208 Further guidance on substitution is provided by HSE's publication *Seven steps to successful substitution of hazardous substances*[68] and *Designing and operating safe chemical reaction processes.*[69]

209 DSEAR deals only with the safety risks from dangerous substances, however, employers should also consider environmental issues relating to dangerous substances and take account of any relevant environmental legislation.

Control and mitigation measures

210 Where risks cannot be completely eliminated through substitution, an employer should use a combination of control and mitigation measures to ensure the safety of employees and others.

211 In existing work situations, the current control and mitigation measures should be carefully reviewed, in the light of experience and improved, extended, or replaced as necessary to ensure that they are achieving, and sustaining the necessary level of risk reduction.

212 The measures selected should be appropriate to the nature of the work activity, consistent with the risk assessment and sufficient to reduce the overall risk so far as is reasonably practicable. This is particularly important where an explosive atmosphere contains a mixture of dangerous substances either in the same form, eg different combustible dusts, or in different forms, eg gases or vapours.

213 Regulation 6(4) sets out a number of control measures in a priority order aimed at ensuring safety 'at source' thereby preventing the dangerous situation happening.

214 In selecting control measures, employers need to consider regulations 6(3) and (4) together. The measures specified in regulation 6(4) should be applied subject to reasonable practicability and the information from the risk assessment, and they should be appropriate to the nature of the activity or operation. This means that employers should consider the application of the measures set out in 6(4)(a) in so far as they are appropriate, before considering those in 6(4)(b) and so on if further action is necessary to reduce risks so far as is reasonably practicable. Measures specified include:

(a)   reducing the quantity of dangerous substances;

(b)   avoiding or minimising releases;

(c)   controlling the release of a dangerous substance at source;

(d)   preventing the formation of explosive atmospheres;

(e)   collecting and containing releases;

(f)   avoiding ignition sources;

(g)   avoiding adverse conditions (eg high temperatures); and

(h)   segregating incompatible substances.

215 The list of measures given in the Regulations is not exhaustive and employers may devise other effective measures in addition to those in regulation 6(4).

216   Mitigation measures are measures that limit the harmful physical effects resulting from a fire or explosion in such a way to reduce risk to persons.

217   Regulation 6(5) sets out a number of mitigation measures including:

(a)   reducing to a minimum the number of employees (and others who may be at risk) exposed;

(b)   providing measures to avoid propagation of fires and explosions;

(c)   providing explosion pressure relief;

(d)   providing explosion suppression;

(e)   providing plant which can withstand an explosion; and

(f)   providing suitable personal protective equipment.

218   The measures, which are not an exhaustive list, should be selected so as to be appropriate to the nature of the work activity, consistent with the risk assessment and sufficiently effective so as to reduce the risk to the required level. They are not in a priority order, and other equally effective mitigation measures may be devised.

219   When devising the solutions for the purposes of control and mitigation measures, it should be taken into account that regulation 6(8) requires that the general safety measures listed in Schedule 1 to DSEAR (eg design of the work process) should be applied, consistent with the risk assessment and appropriate to the nature of the activity or operation.

220   The control measures necessary for the safe handling and use of dangerous substances often require or are dependant on employees carrying out the appropriate operating procedures correctly and complying with written or verbal instructions. Employers, therefore, should provide employees with sufficient supervision and training to ensure that the systems of work required by regulation 6 and Schedule 1 are fully implemented and operating procedures are correctly followed.

Specific issues

Equipment contributing to safety of other equipment in zoned areas

221   The requirements of regulation 6 and Schedule 1 should also be applied to equipment located outside a hazardous place and which contributes to the safe operation of equipment inside a hazardous place. For example, safety instrumented systems, where only the sensors are located in the hazardous area; explosion suppression equipment which depends on a reliable power supply to function correctly; or parts of an explosion relief system outside the equipment to be protected.

222   It should be noted that an explosion in a classified area may affect the safety of workers in an unclassified area, eg an explosion in an item of equipment may endanger someone standing nearby, even though there is normally no flammable material outside the equipment.

Additional information on safety precautions in specific circumstances

223   Further information on specific safety precautions for a variety of activities and circumstances can be found in other ACOP and guidance

documents produced to support DSEAR: *Design of plant, equipment and workplaces,*[2] *Storage of dangerous substances,*[3] *Control and mitigation measures*[4] and *Safe maintenance, repair and cleaning procedures.*[5]

Places where explosive atmospheres may occur

(1)   Every employer shall classify places at the workplace where an explosive atmosphere may occur into hazardous or non-hazardous places in accordance with paragraph 1 of Schedule 2 and shall classify those places so classified as hazardous into zones in accordance with paragraph 2 of that Schedule; and that Schedule shall have effect subject to the notes at the end of that Schedule.

(2)   The employer shall ensure that the requirements specified in Schedule 3 are applied to equipment and protective systems in the places classified as hazardous pursuant to paragraph (1).

(3)   Where necessary, places classified as hazardous pursuant to paragraph (1) shall be marked by the employer with signs at their points of entry in accordance with Schedule 4.

(4)   Before a workplace containing places classified as hazardous pursuant to paragraph (1) is used for the first time, the employer shall ensure that its overall explosion safety is verified by a person who is competent in the field of explosion protection as a result of his experience or any professional training or both.

(5)   The employer shall ensure that appropriate work clothing which does not give rise to electrostatic discharges is provided for use in places classified as hazardous pursuant to paragraph (1).

(6)   This regulation is subject to the transitional provisions in regulation 17(1) to (3).

224   The requirements of regulation 7 apply to places where explosive atmospheres may occur, subject to the exceptions listed in regulation 3(2). Regulation 7 applies in addition to the requirements concerning work processes (which include equipment and protective systems) in regulation 6(8) and Schedule 1.

Classification of areas containing explosive atmospheres

225   Regulation 7 requires areas where explosive atmospheres may occur to be classified into hazardous and non-hazardous workplaces. Any hazardous workplaces should also be classified into zones. Such workplaces and zones should be identified as part of an employer's assessment of risk under regulation 5.

226   Hazardous area classification should be carried out as an integral part of the risk assessment process. Its purpose is to define the extent, frequency and duration of any occurrence of an explosive atmosphere (the zone). The zone in turn defines the requirements for the selection and installation of equipment and protective systems so as to prevent sources of ignition.

227   The controls apply particularly to the selection of fixed equipment that can create an ignition risk; but the same principles may be extended to control the use of mobile equipment; other sources of ignition that may be introduced into the workplace, eg matches and lighters; and the risks from electrostatic discharges.

228 In relation to equipment, in situations where an explosive atmosphere has a high likelihood of occurring, reliance is placed on using equipment designed for that area, ie with a low probability of creating a source of ignition. Conversely, where the likelihood of an explosive atmosphere occurring is reduced, equipment constructed to a less rigorous standard may be used.

229 An international standard, available as BS EN 60079/10,[65] explains the basic principles of area classification for gases and vapours, and its equivalent for dusts has now been published as BS EN 50281:2002.[70] These standards form a suitable basis for assessing the extent and type of zone, and can be used as a guide to complying with regulation 7 and Schedule 2. However, they cannot give the extent and type of zone in any particular case, as site-specific factors should always be taken into account.

230 HSE guidance documents and industry codes contain examples of hazardous areas for a number of different circumstances and, provided they are applied appropriately, they are valuable in encouraging a consistent interpretation of the requirements. Such guidance and codes include: HSG140,[71] HSG51,[72] HSG176,[73] Institute of Petroleum - Model code of safe practice (Part 15: *Area classification code for installations handling flammable fluids*),[74] IP/APEA *Guidance for the design, construction, modification and maintenance of petrol filling stations*,[75] LPGA Code of practice: Part 1 *Bulk LPG storage and fixed installations*,[76] LPGA Code of practice: Part 7 *Storage of full and empty LPG cylinders and cartridges*.[64]

231 Industry specific codes have also been published by various organisations and, provided they are applied appropriately, they are valuable in encouraging a consistent interpretation of the requirements.

232 The conclusions of an area classification study usually take the form of drawings identifying the hazardous areas and types of zones. This is normally supplemented by text giving information about the dangerous substances that will be present, the work activities that have been considered, and other assumptions made by the study. Whenever such drawings and documents have been produced, they should be retained as part of the documentation in support of regulation 5. These documents should be considered whenever new equipment is to be introduced into a zoned area.

233 During a period when maintenance is being carried out the normal area classification drawings may not be applicable. If dangerous substances have been removed, it may be possible to treat areas normally classified as hazardous as non-hazardous. Alternatively, if the maintenance creates a larger than normal risk of a release of a dangerous substance, larger areas may need to be treated as hazardous. It is not normally necessary to create new area classification drawings for the duration of the maintenance work but it may be necessary to implement new temporary controls and procedures as a result of the risk assessment.

Selection of equipment for use in hazardous areas

234 Schedule 2 refers to 'hazardous places' as being places requiring special precautions to protect the health and safety of workers. The area classification standards take this to mean special precautions for the construction, installation and use of equipment so as to control ignition sources. A number of ways of constructing equipment to prevent ignition risks have been published as harmonised standards, and in some cases, additional requirements are set out in the standards relating to installation and use.

235 Schedule 3 requires that equipment and protective systems must be selected on the basis of the requirements set out in the EPS Regulations,[18] unless the risk assessment finds otherwise.

236 The effect of regulation 7, Schedule 2 and Schedule 3, taken together, is to require new equipment and protective systems provided for use at work, in places classified as hazardous, to comply with EPS.[18] In the large majority of cases this can be achieved following an area classification study by selecting EPS equipment of an appropriate category according to the criteria set out in Schedule 3.

237 A standardised marking scheme is widely used to help identify equipment suitable for a specific location. Equipment built to the requirements of EPS[18] will carry the explosion protection symbol 'Ex' in a hexagon, the equipment category number (1, 2, or 3), the letter G and/or D depending on whether it is intended for use in gas or dust atmospheres, and other essential safety information. In many cases this will include a temperature rating expressed as a 'T' marking, and sometimes a gas group. These indicate limitations to safe use. Employers and those installing equipment should consider the marking and documentation provided with 'Ex' equipment when it is being installed.

238 For much electrical equipment, employers will notice comparatively little change from the situation now except in the details of the marking. The EPS Regulations,[18] however, also apply to mechanical equipment that is a potential ignition source. This is a new requirement, and until recently there has been no mechanical equipment that has been 'Ex' marked. A harmonised standard for category 3 mechanical equipment is available as BS EN 13463-1.[77]

239 Schedule 3, however, recognises that there might be circumstances where the risk assessment made under regulation 5 finds that the selection criteria are inappropriate, or unnecessarily restrictive.

240 The phrase 'unless the risk assessment finds otherwise' in Schedule 3 is intended to introduce a degree of flexibility (by way of a derogation from the requirement in paragraph 1 of Schedule 3) to allow equipment of a higher or lower category than that normally required for the zone in question to be used where:

(a)   equipment is temporarily taken into a zoned area and alternative effective precautions are provided to control the risk. An example might be arrangements to isolate or shut down equipment to prevent the release of a dangerous substance;

(b)   workers can be excluded from the hazardous area, and will not be at risk from any ignition of an explosive atmosphere;

(c)   equipment of the required category is simply not available, but a lower category can be used in combination with other protective measures to achieve the purposes of these Regulations.

241 Where employers intend to use the flexibility provided by the derogation, their decision must be fully justified in their assessment of risk and recorded, as the findings are evidently significant. It should also be considered in the context of other requirements placed on employers by these Regulations.

242 In addition, it cannot be used to circumvent the requirements placed on 'responsible persons' under EPS,[18] and in particular:

(a) to allow equipment imported from outside the EU, built to other standards, to be used without complying with the EPS[18] Regulations before it is placed on the market or put into service in the European Economic Area (EEA);

(b) to justify equipment built to lower standards than that specified by EPS.[18]

243 It is important for employers to note that the leeway provided by the DSEAR derogation for employers does not affect the duties placed on manufacturers, suppliers, importers and other 'responsible persons' under the EPS Regulations.[18] Users who manufacture equipment for their own use, or who import directly from outside the EEA are considered to be a 'responsible person' under EPS[18] and take on the full responsibility for complying with those Regulations when putting that equipment into service for the first time in the EEA.

244 Equipment that is 'second-hand' ie it has already been used in the EU prior to July 2003 is not subject to the requirements of Schedule 3 but must meet the relevant requirements set out in regulation 6.

Marking of areas containing explosive atmospheres

245 Regulation 7(3) requires employers to place signs, if necessary, at the entry points of places that have been classified as hazardous (ie zoned areas). The sign to be used is shown in Schedule 4.

246 Regulation 17 says that, where signs are necessary, they should be applied as follows:

(a) at workplaces used for the first time after 30 June 2003, from the date of first use;

(b) at workplaces already in use on 30 June 2003, by 30 June 2006; and

(c) at workplaces already in use on 30 June 2003 which have been modified thereafter, the signs should be applied from the date the modification is made in respect of that modified workplace area.

247 The purpose of signs is to warn of areas where an explosive atmosphere may occur in such a quantity that employees need to be warned of its presence, so that they can take the necessary precautions in relation to the risk. Signs are useful to:

(a) identify places where special workplace or site rules apply eg no smoking, antistatic footwear to be worn, or access restricted to authorised people;

(b) identify where portable or mobile equipment must be of an explosion-protected design eg hand torches, vehicles or cleaning machines;

(c)   identify, for the purposes of audit or later plant modifications, where fixed equipment should be of an explosion-protected design.

248   To decide whether a sign is necessary, employers should refer to the risk assessment made under regulation 5(1). If the assessment indicates that, after appropriate measures have been taken to eliminate or control risks, there is still a significant risk then the sign should be used so as to reduce the risk further. Where there is already sufficient identification of the potential for explosive atmospheres to occur, or if there is no significant risk, an additional Ex sign may not be needed.

249   Where a sign is necessary, it should be positioned at the points of entry to the place where the explosive atmosphere may exist. Where an explosive atmosphere may occur within a clearly defined area, the appropriate point or points of entry will be easy to determine. However, in other cases explosive atmospheres may occur in places that do not have obvious entry points, for example in multiple places around a large open-air chemical plant. Such places are often already identified in other ways, for example by painted lines on the ground to indicate hazard zones. Signs may, therefore, not always be appropriate but the risk area must be identified and its presence communicated by some other means.

250   Where a sign or signs are considered necessary to further reduce risk, in addition to other measures, it may be more appropriate in some cases just to mark points of entry to the workplace as a whole, rather than the numerous individual locations within the site as well, if all the special precautions apply throughout the entire site.

251   The size of any signs provided should be sufficient to fulfil their warning function, and they should be maintained so that they are clearly visible. The arrangements made by employers under regulation 9 should ensure that employees receive sufficient information, instruction and training on the meaning of the sign and the measures to be taken in connection with it.

252   The requirement in regulation 7(3) applies in addition and without prejudice to similar requirements in other legislation, such as the Dangerous Substances (Notification and Marking of Sites) Regulations[78] and the Health and Safety (Safety Signs and Signals) Regulations 1996.[79] If signs have already been provided under those Regulations, and they are sufficient to warn of an explosive atmosphere, then the addition of the sign specified in Schedule 4 may not be necessary. However, if the employer considers the existing signs are not sufficient the sign in Schedule 4 may need to be applied in addition.

Verification of places containing explosive atmospheres

253   After 30 June 2003, if a workplace contains places that are or will be classified as hazardous, under regulation 7(1) the employer must ensure that work equipment in the hazardous area is safe, protective systems associated with these areas are suitable, and that work activities have been designed so they can be carried out safely, before the workplace is first used. These actions collectively are termed verification. Some parts of these verification checks can be carried out at an early stage, for example, critical design calculations could be independently assessed. Other aspects of verification can only be completed when a plant is built, eg physical checks of equipment installed against design drawings.

254   The purpose of verifying overall explosion safety is to confirm the workplace can operate in accordance with these Regulations. The workplace

should not be brought into use if the verification shows that explosion risks are such that it is not safe to do so.

255   Verification should include consideration of the following:

(a)   the dangerous substances that will be present at the workplace, including their hazardous properties and quantity;

(b)   the suitability of the plant, equipment and protective systems for work in explosive atmospheres;

(c)   the work processes, operating procedures and systems of work;

(d)   the effectiveness of measures to:

- prevent explosive atmospheres forming;

- control risks from explosive atmospheres;

- mitigate the effects of an explosion;

(e)   the effectiveness of emergency arrangements where these are required.

256   Verification can be carried out through a variety of means, for example by an examination of documents, visual inspection, or physical checks and measurements. Much of the work may be a normal part of the commissioning process. Examples of the work involved could include:

(a)   checks that mechanical ventilation systems produce the air flows intended;

(b)   inspection of records showing that process equipment is leak-tight before dangerous substances are introduced for the first time;

(c)   ensuring that a hazardous area classification drawing has been prepared, and a visual inspection that electrical equipment is of the correct type or category for the zone where it has been installed and has been installed correctly;

(d)   ensuring that appropriate information is available about the dangerous properties of materials to be handled in the plant.

257   Any documents produced during verification may be useful as part of the risk assessment required under regulation 5(1), but equally, if some aspects of the risk assessment are completed at an early stage, they may be useful in identifying what should be checked at the verification stage. Where a workplace is subject to legislation on major hazards, such as COMAH,[26] the information obtained for the preparation of a safety report or other documentation is considered similarly relevant for the purpose of explosion safety verification.

258   There is no requirement to keep a record of the verification. However, it is good practice to record the name of the person carrying out the verification, and the date on which it was completed. If a record is kept it can be in a written or electronic form. Any documentation produced may be useful for the risk assessment, especially where verification indicates that specific conditions need to be maintained to ensure explosion safety. These conditions should be included in the risk assessment record.

259 Regulation 5(3) requires any risk assessment to be kept under review, for example when new processes are started, or new work equipment is brought into use. Part of that review might involve verification of a significant new plant or process, but it is not intended that verification be applied to every change in a work activity or equipment.

260 The employer must ensure that someone who is competent to consider the risks at that workplace and decide on the adequacy of the control and other measures to ensure explosion safety carries out the verification. The installer of new equipment, the final user, or an independent person may carry out the verification. On larger installations more than one person may need to be involved.

261 Whoever is selected must have obtained sufficient practical and theoretical knowledge from actual experience and/or professional training relevant to the particular workplace and work activity they intend to verify. For example, a person who is competent to verify the explosion safety of a petrol station may not be competent to verify the adequacy of measures to deal with combustible dust in a textile factory.

Antistatic clothing

262 Some clothing, including footwear, contains materials that can generate electrostatic discharges during use. Such discharges can ignite certain types of explosive atmospheres.

263 The risk from electrostatic discharges from clothing can be reduced if the wearer is earthed by means of suitable footwear and flooring, such as concrete or steel grids. This is likely to be sufficient for places classified into zone 0, 1 or 2 as specified in Schedule 2. In a small number of cases special footwear may also be necessary for zones 20, 21 and 22.

264 After 30 June 2003, employees working in explosive atmospheres formed by gases or vapours should be provided with antistatic footwear if the assessment carried out under regulation 5(1) indicates that electrostatic discharges could ignite the atmosphere. This is also necessary for some types of dust that are very easily ignited. In addition, the employer should ensure that the floor is not highly insulating. Usually, these measures are sufficient to control the ignition risk. Other antistatic work clothing must also be provided if the risk assessment shows this to be necessary.

265 General advice on the electrostatic hazards is contained in Part 1 of BS 5958:1991,[80] and Part 2 includes a range of measures applicable to various industrial situations such as petrochemical installations and flammable powder handling. Further information can also be found in the BSI report PD CLC/TR 50404:2003 Electrostatics - Code of Practice for the avoidance of hazards due to static electricity.[81]

266 The employer must also ensure that any personal protective equipment provided for other purposes, such as to prevent contact with substances hazardous to health, which may also be used in an explosive atmosphere will not create electrostatic discharges. Antistatic or ordinary clothing should not be removed in places where an explosive atmosphere may occur and a safe area should be established where workers are able to remove or change clothing, etc in safety.

267 Employers need to be aware that electrostatic risks can be created by personal items brought into a hazardous area, and may need to provide instructions for employees or visitors.

268 Where necessary, employers should also ensure that visitors to their premises also have appropriate antistatic clothing.

Arrangements to deal with accidents, incidents and emergencies

(1) *Subject to paragraph (4), in order to protect the safety of his employees from an accident, incident or emergency related to the presence of a dangerous substance at the workplace, the employer shall ensure that -*

(a) *procedures, including the provision of appropriate first-aid facilities and relevant safety drills (which shall be tested at regular intervals), have been prepared which can be put into effect when such an event occurs;*

(b) *information on emergency arrangements, including -*

(i) *details of relevant work hazards and hazard identification arrangements, and*

(ii) *specific hazards likely to arise at the time of an accident, incident or emergency,*

is available;

(c) *suitable warning and other communication systems are established to enable an appropriate response, including remedial actions and rescue operations, to be made immediately when such an event occurs;*

(d) *where necessary, before any explosion conditions are reached, visual, or audible, warnings are given and employees withdrawn; and*

(e) *where the risk assessment indicates it is necessary, escape facilities are provided and maintained to ensure that, in the event of danger, employees can leave endangered places promptly and safely.*

(2) *Subject to paragraph (4), the employer shall ensure that information on the matters referred to in paragraph (1)(a), (c) to (e) and the information required by paragraph 1(b) is -*

(a) *made available to relevant accident and emergency services to enable those services, whether internal or external to the workplace, to prepare their own response procedures and precautionary measures; and*

(b) *displayed at the workplace, unless the results of the risk assessment make this unnecessary.*

(3) *Subject to paragraph (4), in the event of an accident, incident or emergency related to the presence of a dangerous substance at the workplace, the employer shall ensure that -*

(a) *immediate steps are taken to -*

(i) *mitigate the effects of the event,*

(ii) *restore the situation to normal, and*

(iii) *inform those of his employees who may be affected; and*

(b) only those persons who are essential for the carrying out of repairs and other necessary work are permitted in the affected area and they are provided with -

(i) appropriate personal protective equipment and protective clothing; and

(ii) any necessary specialised safety equipment and plant,

which shall be used until the situation is restored to normal.

(4) Paragraphs (1) to (3) shall not apply where -

(a) the results of the risk assessment show that, because of the quantity of each dangerous substance at the workplace, there is only a slight risk to employees; and

(b) the measures taken by the employer to comply with his duty under regulation 6(1) are sufficient to control that risk.

Overall approach

269 An accident, incident or emergency is any unplanned event which has the potential to cause harm and which may require the evacuation, escape or rescue of one or more people.

270 DSEAR requires employers to assess the likelihood, and scale or magnitude of the effects that may result from any foreseeable accident, incident, emergency or other event involving dangerous substances present at the workplace. On the basis of this assessment, employers should put in place appropriate emergency arrangements to safeguard people on their premises, mitigate the effects of any such event and restore the situation to normal.

271 The precautions to deal with accidents, incidents and emergencies are without prejudice to the precautions to be taken to eliminate and reduce risk as required by regulation 6. The possibility of such events is minimised by good plant design and layout, sound engineering and good operating practice, and proper instruction and training of personnel. However, in spite of these measures, accidents, incidents and emergencies can still occur and therefore appropriate procedures are required to manage these.

272 It is not expected that employers will necessarily be able to achieve full mitigation of all foreseeable accidents, incidents and emergencies solely by their own means. Rather, it will typically be a combination of the workplace emergency arrangements and those of the emergency services that will provide, overall, the safety of employees and other people. The fire service will in any case assume responsibility for tackling any fire upon their arrival, but they may also be able to assist in dealing with other non-fire emergencies such as released or spilled dangerous substances.

273 The primary requirement for protecting workers is to ensure that they are able to evacuate or be evacuated to a place of safety. The requirement to mitigate the effects of the accident, incident or emergency should have regard to this objective and to the need not to expose people to any unnecessary risks. In many cases evacuation of people to a safe place will be the correct course of action. Particular attention should be given in choosing the safe place to ensure that it will not be affected by the event should it escalate. Employers will also need to take account of situations where toxic substances may be released as a result of an incident.

274 Employers are expected to take reasonable steps to ensure that they have sufficient knowledge to properly carry out the assessment. For example, by referring to appropriate sources of information, including relevant guidance, trade information and advice from manufacturers/suppliers. It is important for employers to consult with their employees and their representatives (including safety and trade union representatives) during the assessment process and when procedures are being drawn up.

275 Employers should also liaise as necessary with the relevant accident and emergency services on the assistance they can provide.

Slight risk

276 Employers are not required to make these additional emergency arrangements where they assess that there is only a slight risk because of the quantity of each substance present and the control measures they have put in place to fulfil the requirements of other safety or fire legislation are sufficient to control that risk. For example, in respect of fire, the normal emergency procedures, including escape routes and means of giving warning already provided in the workplace may be assessed to be sufficient. Appropriate guidance on fire precautions in such circumstances is available in *Fire safety: An employer's guide*.[67]

277 Employers must be satisfied, however, that those control measures will continue to be effective if an accident, incident or emergency occurs. For example, where an accompanying event such as an explosion is possible that might compromise an escape route, regard would need to be given to the alternative measures needed to ensure safe evacuation. For example, this might include a specially strengthened escape route and/or refuge.

278 In order to decide whether the risk is slight, employers should take into account:

(a)   the quantity of each dangerous substance;

(b)   the work activity involving that dangerous substance;

(c)   information from the risk assessment carried out under regulation 5(1);

(d)   the potential scale of any release;

(e)   interactions between substances; and

(f)   the effect of the measures taken under regulation 6 to reduce the risk.

Assessing the risks

279 Employers should adopt a systematic approach for identifying potential accidents, incidents, emergencies or other events and consider how they can be detected when they have occurred, or are occurring. They also need to determine, for the various stages of the accident, incident or emergency, the appropriate intervention to both mitigate the consequences of the event and prevent its further escalation. The impact of an accident, incident or emergency can often be greatly reduced if prompt and correct action is taken as soon as the event occurs.

280 Employers will need to determine the degree of intervention appropriate to the circumstances of the emergency. This could range from those with

sophisticated response teams who have been specially trained and equipped to deal with emergencies to those who will undertake minimal intervention at the workplace, but instead rely on the external emergency services.

281 Factors to be taken into account by employers when assessing the requirements for emergency arrangements include:

(a) the properties of the dangerous substances present, and their quantities and the way they are used or stored;

(b) the foreseeable types of accidents, incidents, emergencies or other events that may occur, and the level of risk that may be presented (for example, the response required to deal with a major fire in a bulk storage facility will be different from that required for a small spill of a few litres of flammable liquid);

(c) precursors to the end emergency (fire or explosion) involving the dangerous substance (eg unignited leaks, spills and releases of the dangerous substance; or the potential for these, arising for example, from mechanical damage to plant containing dangerous substances);

(d) means of detecting events - for example the selection and effectiveness of the means of detecting a leak, spill or release of a dangerous substance and hence the speed and nature of the emergency response will depend on such matters as location, size of release and potential escalating events;

(e) the trigger events for alarms and warnings - for example where mechanical exhaust ventilation is provided to ensure a safe atmosphere, it might well be considered reasonable that critical diminution in its flow should cause an alarm or suitable warning to be given, so that emergency actions can be taken to isolate the release of the dangerous substance and take other remedial action as necessary;

(f) the role of the non-employees in emergency arrangements - for example a spill outdoors during a driver controlled tanker unloading operation. In this case it would be reasonable for the driver (who may not be an employee) to detect the spill and initiate appropriate emergency action which might include warning other people in the locality, using spill control equipment and calling the emergency services;

(g) specific procedures that employees and others should follow if an accident, incident or emergency occurs (eg clearing up spills of flammable liquids or, for more serious incidents, moving to a safe area or complete evacuation of the workplace);

(h) the role, responsibilities and authority of employees who may be allocated specific duties (eg persons responsible for shutting down equipment, checking that specific areas have been successfully evacuated, contacting the emergency services, etc);

(i) the provision, where necessary, of suitable safety equipment or personal protective equipment; and

(j) procedures for assisting particular groups of people, such as members of the public or other visitors on site (who may be unfamiliar with the workplace and the risks presented by dangerous substances that are present) or disabled employees.

First aid

282 Depending on the findings of the risk assessment and measures already taken, employers will need to consider what additional first aid facilities may need to be provided (including appropriately trained first-aiders). The level and nature of these facilities will need to take account of the likely effects of any accident, incident or emergency. Employers are also required to provide first aid facilities under the Health and Safety (First Aid) Regulations 1981.[82]

Safety drills

283 Depending on the findings of the risk assessment and measures already taken, employers will also need to consider what additional safety drills may need to be developed (and tested). The frequency of practicing any such drills will depend on a number of factors including;

(a)   the quantity of dangerous substances on site and the level of risk they present;

(b)   the size of the workplace and workforce; and

(c)   the success, or otherwise of previous tests.

Warning and communication systems

284 Warning and communication systems (including visual and audible alarms) should be provided to alert people to an actual or potential incident involving dangerous substances. The system should be appropriate to the level of risk presented by foreseeable accidents, incidents or emergencies and provide sufficient time and information to allow the necessary emergency actions to be carried out.

285 When considering what warning and communication systems will be appropriate, employers should take into account:

(a)   the size of their workplace and workforce;

(b)   who needs to be alerted and why;

(c)   quantities of substances involved and the level and type of risk those substances present; and

(d)   the emergency actions to be taken in the event of an incident and the required response times for these.

286 The warning system should not require persons to remain in the affected area to give the alarm during an emergency. Examples of warning systems include:

(a)   a continuous or intermittent ringing bell;

(b)   a klaxon or hooter;

(c)   warning lights;

(d)   an intercom or tannoy system.

287 Warning systems are not necessarily restricted to signalling the need for withdrawal or evacuation of people who might be affected by the incident.

They can also be to alert employees of an incident or emergency, so that they can take appropriate emergency action to contain or mitigate the incident. Where there are multiple alarm systems in a work place, employers should ensure that these are clearly discernible and that their employees have the necessary training and equipment to be able to safely carry out the correct actions required.

288 Employers should ensure that any warning or communication system can be seen or heard in all parts of the workplace likely to be affected by the incident. Employers should also have procedures in place to keep employees informed of situations as they develop and any actions that may be needed as a consequence.

Escape facilities

289 Employers should ensure through the risk assessment that adequate escape facilities are provided to enable employees and any other persons present to readily and safely reach a place of safety.

290 The presence of a dangerous substance can significantly enhance the speed at which a fire develops and also the amount of smoke and fume evolved. When considering escape facilities employers should consider the potential for explosions, rapid fire development and ingress of dangerous substances into escape routes to compromise escape. Employers should consider how these events may be prevented and/or mitigated in such circumstances, eg by appropriate design of the escape route and/or means of suppressing or containing the fire.

291 Employers should consider the provision of adequate escape facilities in parallel with the requirement contained in the FPW Regulations.[13]

Mitigation measures and restoring the situation to normal

292 Employers must implement those measures necessary to achieve control or containment of an accident, incident or emergency in order to allow sufficient time for people to escape or be evacuated to a place of safety. Following an event, employers must assess whether any danger remains and implement the necessary measures to make the situation safe. If there are any doubts, expert assistance should be sought, eg from accident and emergency services. Implementation of the necessary measures should be achieved without exposing employees or others to unnecessary risk. However this needs to be balanced against the overall risk to people of doing nothing or taking only limited measures.

293 Steps to mitigate the effects of an incident may, where it is safe to do so, include:

(a) evacuating people who may be affected, taking into account possible escalation of the incident, to a place of safety;

(b) isolating plant or equipment from where uncontrolled releases of a dangerous substance are occurring;

(c) removing to a safe place the dangerous substance under threat;

(d) preventing the further spread of spilt or leaking dangerous substance by the use of barriers, booms or absorbent materials;

(e) limiting the extent of any flammable vapour cloud arising from a release of the dangerous substance by, for example, the use of water sprays and curtains, or applying fire fighting foam over the surface of the spilt or leaking liquid materials;

(f)   increasing natural or mechanical ventilation to dilute hazardous concentrations of dangerous substances arising from an incident;

(g)   controlling potential ignition sources in non-hazardous areas that are now affected by an uncontrolled release of dangerous substance;

(h)   protecting the vessels or plant containing the dangerous substance against the effects of fire by such means as water deluge systems, water monitors and passive fire protection coatings; and

(i)   applying appropriate fire-fighting materials to a fire involving a dangerous substance.

294   Under regulation 8, measures to restore the situation to normal following an event are limited to those measures needed to achieve the normal level of safety for the premises. They do not include measures to rebuild a plant or restore it to normal production or operation but could include:

(a)   repair or decommissioning leaking or unsafe plant;

(b)   safe recovery and clean up of spilt or leaked dangerous substances;

(c)   making safe damaged or unstable buildings;

(d)   repair or replacement of any equipment, monitoring devices or alarms necessary for the safety of employers or others present on the premises;

(e)   neutralising or disposing of any unstable or dangerous substances resulting from an incident.

Persons carrying out repairs and other necessary work

295   Measures taken to deal with accidents, incidents and emergencies will need to be adaptable to deal with the specific situation. This will similarly be the case with the remedial action following the accident, incident or emergency. It is therefore imperative for employers to ensure: that those of their employees expected to respond in the event of an accident, incident or emergency involving a dangerous substance have the necessary skills, expertise and training to carry out the functions expected of them; and that suitable plant and equipment necessary to carry out these functions is available and properly maintained for immediate use.

296   Equipment to be provided should include appropriate personal protective equipment (PPE) (including appropriate protective clothing and footwear) that is determined to be necessary to enable employees to safely carry out the emergency actions required. However, employees should not be exposed to unnecessary risk in carrying these out.

297   When selecting equipment to be used in emergencies, employers will need to ensure it is appropriate for the circumstances in which it may be used. For example the need to avoid ignition sources when dealing with the releases of flammable vapours, gases, etc.

298   Before carrying out any remedial work the employer should carry out a risk assessment to determine the control measures that need to be put in place

to ensure the health and safety of employees. As part of this assessment the employer should determine the appropriate systems of work, including possible permit-to-work systems that need to be implemented before employees or contractors enter any areas affected by the incident or emergency. Further information on systems of work is contained in paragraph 24 of the ACOP on *Safe maintenance, repair and cleaning procedures.*[5]

Making information available to employees and the emergency services

299 Information on emergency arrangements should be made available to employees and their representatives. For example, this may be by the periodic circulation of copies of the arrangements, or providing individual copies. The employer should also provide employees with appropriate training and instruction on the emergency arrangements and the adequacy of these should be regularly tested and any deficiencies found as a consequence addressed. Unless the risk assessment indicates otherwise, employers should also display the emergency procedures in a prominent position at key locations in the workplace. Appropriate information on emergency arrangements should also be communicated to non-employees who may be affected.

300 Sufficient information on the nature of any foreseeable emergencies involving dangerous substances should be made available to the relevant accident and emergency services who are likely to be asked to deal with such incidents. As a minimum, employers should contact the external emergency services and offer to make this information available. Employers should also make this information available to any on-site emergency services.

301 Information on the employers' emergency arrangements will help the emergency services to prepare their own response procedures and precautionary measures to be followed in the event of an incident occurring at the workplace. If requested by the emergency services, employers should be prepared to send the information to them and/or meet with their representatives to discuss the emergency procedures. It is also useful to provide details of the employers' designated contact who will advise the emergency services of the situation on their arrival at an emergency. Employers should also keep the emergency services updated on significant changes, such as the quantities and nature of dangerous substances present.

302 Employers will need to consider which external emergency services need to be aware of their emergency arrangements. External emergency services include the fire service, ambulance service and the police. In some cases all may need to be informed. In some circumstances other emergency services may need to be included, for example the coastguard for offshore installations, etc.

303 The information made available should include:

(a) the identity, location and approximate quantities of dangerous substances;

(b) the foreseeable types of accident, incident or emergency that could occur and the hazards that may result;

(c) where on site such events could occur, what effects they could have, other areas that may be affected should the event escalate and the possible repercussion that may cause; and

(d) the emergency arrangements drawn up by the employer to deal with accidents, incidents and emergencies, the procedures prepared by the employer to deal with any such event, the warnings and other communication systems, and escape facilities.

304 In addition to external emergency services, employers should also make this information available to any on-site emergency services.

Review of arrangements

305 The emergency arrangements will need to be reviewed and, if necessary, revised if circumstances change at the workplace. For example, if there is a significant increase in the use of a dangerous substance or if new work processes lead to the introduction of new substances into the workplace.

Relationship of regulation 8 with other legislation

306 In addition to the requirements in these Regulations, the MHSW Regulations[11] and FPW Regulations[13] make wide-ranging and general requirements for assessment of potential emergencies, etc (including fire) and for appropriate measures to be implemented to deal with these. In respect of the dangers arising from an accident, incident or emergency involving the dangerous substance, compliance with regulation 8 of DSEAR fulfils most of the requirements of regulation 8 of the MHSW Regulations. For example, the MHSW Regulations contain additional requirements to nominate competent persons to initiate procedures.

307 Other health and safety at work legislation also include requirements on planning for and responding to emergencies. These include:

(a) COMAH,[26] which deal with workplaces where specific quantities of dangerous substances are present;

(b) PFEER,[27] which set out emergency arrangements and responses in the offshore sector; and

(c) the Radiation (Emergency Preparedness and Public Information) Regulations 2001 (REPPIR),[83] may also apply as some substances with radioactive properties may be dangerous substances for DSEAR purposes.

308 In consequence, the assessment of accidents, incidents and emergencies related to the presence of a dangerous substance and the determination of emergency arrangements to be taken as result of these, should be performed at the same time as the requirements of the above Regulations, plus those of any other relevant health, safety and fire legislation. In practice meeting the requirements in this other legislation (with regard to flammable properties, etc) may mean that an employer is largely meeting the requirements in DSEAR.

309 The emergency measures under DSEAR deal with safety risks. Employers will also need to consider whether such arrangements are also required to address health risks under COSHH.[14]

Interface with fire safety legislation

310 To avoid duplication with existing fire safety legislation (enforced by the fire authorities), the FPW Regulations[13] have been amended via DSEAR to make specific provisions of DSEAR part of the workplace fire precautions legislation. This amendment to the FPW Regulations makes the fire authority

the enforcing authority for regulations 1-6, 8, 9 and 11 of DSEAR, in so far as they relate to general fire safety matters (eg means of escape).

Information, instruction and training

(1) Where a dangerous substance is present at the workplace, the employer shall provide his employees with -

(a) suitable and sufficient information, instruction and training on the appropriate precautions and actions to be taken by the employee in order to safeguard himself and other employees at the workplace;

(b) the details of any such substance including -

(i) the name of the substance and the risk which it presents;

(ii) access to any relevant safety data sheet; and

(iii) legislative provisions which concern the hazardous properties of the substance; and

(c) the significant findings of the risk assessment.

(2) The information, instruction and training required by paragraph (1) shall be -

(a) adapted to take account of significant changes in the type of work carried out or methods of work used by the employer; and

(b) provided in a manner appropriate to the risk assessment.

311 The information provided to employees and, to the extent that it is required by the nature and degree of the risk, to other people who may be present at a workplace, should include the following:

(a) the identity of any dangerous substances which could present risks to safety, including where they are used;

(b) the type and extent of those risks, including factors that may increase the risk, eg smoking or other ignition sources - much of this information will also be included in any relevant safety data sheets to which employees must be given access;

(c) the significant findings of the risk assessment;

(d) the control/mitigation measures adopted, including methods of work, the reasons for them, and how to use them properly;

(e) any further relevant information resulting from a review of the assessment: why it has been done and how any changes will affect the way employees do the work in the future; and

(f) any procedures for dealing with accidents, incidents and emergencies prepared in accordance with regulation 8.

312 The employer must also make information available to employees or their representatives in accordance with the: Health and Safety (Consultation with Employees) Regulations 1996;[24] the Safety

Representatives and Safety Committees Regulations 1977;[23] and the Offshore Installations (Safety Representatives and Safety Committees) Regulations 1989.[84]

313 Training and instruction should include elements of theory as well as practice. Training in the use and application of control measures and equipment should be carried out taking into account recommendations and instructions supplied by the manufacturer.

314 Regulations 8 and 9 of PUWER[20] also include requirements for information, instructions and training.

315 The objective in providing information, instruction and training is to ensure that employees can work with dangerous substances without putting themselves or others at risk. The extent of the information, instruction and training required will vary with the degree of complexity of the hazards, risks, processes and controls. The risk assessment will identify these but where a substance is being used that is not particularly dangerous and risks are adequately controlled, basic instructions and training may be all that is required.

316 The employer should consider all the various ways of providing information, instruction and training and select those most appropriate to their own circumstances. Options include: class or group tuition, individual tuition, written instructions including leaflets, courses etc. New employees will require proper induction training which should always cover emergency and evacuation procedures.

317 The information, instruction and training provided should be pitched appropriately, given the level of training, knowledge and experience of employees. It should be provided in a form which takes account of any language difficulties or disabilities. Information can be provided in whatever form is most suitable in the circumstances, as long as it can be understood by everyone. For employees with little or no understanding of English, or those who cannot read English, employers may need to make special arrangements. These could include providing translation, using interpreters, or replacing written notes with clearly understood symbols or diagrams.

Training and information for non-employees

318 Employers also need to take account of the needs of people other than employees who may be present on site, such as members of the public, etc. While it may not always be practical to provide formal training in these circumstances, employers should consider what other information or instruction may be needed to reduce risks, such as signs and notices explaining hazards (eg warning notices, no smoking signs, etc), and copies of emergency and evacuation procedures.

319 Information, instruction and training in relation to risks from dangerous substances need only be provided to non-employees where it is required to ensure their safety. For example, in situations where the number and type of visitors to a workplace, or the short duration of the visit, combined with a negligible risk, make the provision of such information inappropriate (such as customers in a shop or passengers on an aircraft), it would not be required. However, where it is provided, it should be in proportion to the level and type of risk.

320   Where employees from one employer work on the premises of another, the employer occupying the premises must provide the other employer with sufficient information about any dangerous substances that may be present at the premises as part of the day-to-day activity. This information should be sufficiently detailed to allow the other employer to provide his own employees with information and any appropriate instruction on complying with the occupying employer's measures.

321   The employer occupying the premises will also need to know about any dangerous substances that are likely to be used or produced by the work the other employer will be doing. This information is important as it allows the occupying employer to:

(a)   be satisfied that the measures put in place by the employer doing the work will not only protect that employer's employees from risks presented by the substances concerned, but also the occupier's own employees;

(b)   provide his own employees with information and instruction about any dangerous substances that the other employer will be using or the work will produce; and

(c)   reassure his employees that any risks to their safety are being properly controlled.

322   Employers should also take steps to ensure that members of the emergency services attending in the event of an incident (in particular, fire fighters) are made aware of any substances on the premises which offer a significant risk to their safety (see regulation 8 - Arrangements to deal with accidents, incidents and emergencies).

Updating information, instruction and training

323   Information, instruction and training will need to be reviewed and if necessary updated whenever changes are made to the type of work carried out or to the work methods used. Such changes could include the amount of substances used or produced, new control measures, new substances brought into the workplace, automation of certain processes, etc. Employers should look at the circumstances of their workplace and decide whether refresher training or updated information is needed and if so, when it should be given.

Identification of hazardous contents of containers and pipes

Where containers and pipes used at work for dangerous substances are not marked in accordance with relevant requirements of the legislation listed in Schedule 5, the employer shall, subject to any derogations provided for in that legislation, ensure that the contents of those containers and pipes, together with the nature of those contents and any associated hazards, are clearly identifiable.

324   This regulation applies to containers and pipes that contain dangerous substances that are not subject to or exempt from any marking requirements in the legislation listed in Schedule 5.

325   Identification of pipes and containers, particularly those that are visible, alerts employees and others to the presence of a dangerous substance so that

they can take the necessary precautions. Identification can also help to avoid confusion over contents and thereby avoid incorrect mixing of contents.

326 The Regulations do not specify the means of identification. Suitable means could include labelling, the use of appropriate colour coding or providing instructions and training.

327 The most appropriate means of identification will depend on the nature of the work activity. For example, in situations where contents may change regularly (eg test tubes in laboratories, chemical process vessels and pipes which are not dedicated to one substance) it may not be practical to use labelling. In these cases employers will need other arrangements to ensure that employees are aware of the hazards associated with the substances involved - employers could, for example, provide suitable process instruction sheets, record sheets or training for employees.

328 For the purpose of this Regulation a container includes any fixed or portable, open or enclosed, means to contain dangerous substances such as tanks, silos, reaction vessels, and waste receptacles together with any associated pipe runs or piping system.

329 Identification is not necessary where the substance contained is a bulk solid product, such as flour, which is not itself a dangerous substance and is only hazardous if released and dispersed in the air.

Duty of co-ordination

Where two or more employers share the same workplace (whether on a temporary or a permanent basis) where an explosive atmosphere may occur, the employer responsible for the workplace shall co-ordinate the implementation of all the measures required by these Regulations to be taken to protect employees from any risk from the explosive atmosphere.

330 Where there are two or more employers sharing a workplace, regulation 11 requires the employer responsible for the workplace to co-ordinate the implementation of measures taken under DSEAR to protect employees and others at the workplace from risks from explosive atmospheres. This duty comes into effect on 30 June 2003.

331 The duty of co-ordination applies to individual workplaces. Workplaces that are part of multi-occupancy buildings or sites where each unit is under the control of an individual tenant employer or self-employed persons are regarded as separate workplaces. In some cases, however, the common parts of such multi-occupancy sites may be shared (eg a common reception area), or may be under the control of a person to whom section 4 of the HSW Act[8] applies and suitable arrangements may need to be put in place for these areas.

332 In shared premises, such as in dock areas or airports, it may be the employer responsible for the workplace or one of the other employers who shares the premises whose work activity creates the explosive atmosphere. Effective co-ordination will require the responsible employer for the workplace to obtain sufficient information from all employers at the workplace about the nature of their work activity, whether any dangerous substances are likely to be present, and the likelihood of an explosive atmosphere occurring. All employers at the workplace should provide the responsible employer with the information required and assist in assessing the shared risks and implementing any necessary safety measures.

333 The aim of co-ordination is to:

(a) alert other employers, employees and others at the workplace to the presence of hazardous places or substances used by another employer;

(b) ensure that suitable control and mitigation measures are in place;

(c) ensure employees and others have sufficient training, etc (see regulation 9); and

(d) facilitate emergency arrangements in the event of an incident.

334 The employer responsible for the workplace should record the 'aim of co-ordination' in the risk assessment as well as the measures and procedures for implementing it required by regulation 5(4).

Extension outside Great Britain

These Regulations shall apply outside Great Britain as sections 1 to 59 and 80 to 82 of the 1974 Act apply by virtue of the Health and Safety at Work etc. Act 1974 (Application outside Great Britain) Order 2001[a].

Exemption certificates

(1)   Subject to paragraph (2), the Health and Safety Executive may, by a certificate in writing, exempt any person or class of persons or any dangerous substance or class of dangerous substances from all or any of the requirements or prohibitions imposed by or under these Regulations and any such exemption may be granted subject to conditions and to a limit of time and may be revoked at any time by a certificate in writing.

(2)   The Health and Safety Executive shall not grant any such exemption unless, having regard to the circumstances of the case, and in particular to -

(a)   the conditions, if any, which it proposes to attach to the exemption; and

(b)   any requirements imposed by or under any enactments which apply to the case,

it is satisfied that the health and safety of persons who are likely to be affected by the exemption will not be prejudiced in consequence of it and that the exemption will be compatible with the requirements of the Directives.

(3)   For the purposes of paragraph (2), "the Directives" means Council Directive 98/24/EC on the protection of the health and safety of workers from the risks related to chemical agents at work[b] and Council Directive 99/92/EC on minimum requirements for improving the safety and health protection of workers potentially at risk from explosive atmospheres[c].

(a) S.I. 2001/2127
(b) OJ No. L 131, 5.9.98, p.11
(c) OJ No. L 23, 28.1.00, p.57

Exemptions for Ministry of Defence etc

(1) In this regulation -

(a) "Her Majesty's Forces" means any of the naval, military or air forces of the Crown, whether raised inside or outside the United Kingdom and whether any such force is a regular, auxiliary or reserve force, and includes any civilian employed by those forces;

(b) "visiting force" has the same meaning as it does for the purposes of any provision of Part 1 of the Visiting Forces Act 1952[(a)]; and

(c) "headquarters" means a headquarters for the time being specified in Schedule 2 to the Visiting Forces and International Headquarters (Application of Law) Order 1999[(b)].

(2) The Secretary of State for Defence may, in the interests of national security, by a certificate in writing, exempt -

(a) any of Her Majesty's Forces,

(b) any visiting force,

(c) any member of a visiting force working in or attached to a headquarters, or

(d) any person engaged in work involving dangerous substances, if that person is under the direct supervision of a representative of the Secretary of State for Defence,

from all or any of the requirements or prohibitions imposed by these Regulations and any such exemption may be granted subject to conditions and to a limit of time and may be revoked at any time by a certificate in writing, except that, where any such exemption is granted, suitable arrangements shall be made for the assessment of the risk to safety created by the work involving dangerous substances and for adequately controlling the risk to persons to whom the exemption relates.

(a) 1952 c.67 (15 & 16 Geo 6 & 1 Eliz 2)
(b) S.I. 1999/1736

Amendments

(1) The Acts and instruments referred to in Part 1 of Schedule 6 shall be amended in accordance with that Part.

(2) The instruments referred to in Part 2 of Schedule 6 shall be amended in accordance with that Part.

335 This regulation brings Schedule 6 into force. This contains amendments to legislation (mainly concerning petrol).

Repeals and revocations

(1)   The Act and instruments referred to in column 1 of Part 1 of Schedule 7 shall be repealed or revoked to the extent specified in the corresponding entry in column 3 of that Part.

(2)   The Act and instruments referred to in column 1 of Part 2 of Schedule 7 shall be repealed or revoked to the extent specified in the corresponding entry in column 3 of that Part.

336   This regulation brings Schedule 7 into force. This fully or partly repeals or revokes some pieces of earlier legislation.

Transitional provisions

(1)   The requirements of regulation 7(2) and Schedule 3 shall not apply to equipment and protective systems for use in places where explosive atmospheres may occur which are or have been in use or made available at the workplace on or before 30th June 2003.

(2)   Subject to paragraphs (1) and (3), a workplace which contains places where explosive atmospheres may occur -

(a)   which is or has been in use on or before 30th June 2003 shall comply with the requirements of regulations 7 and 11 no later than 30th June 2006 and the employer's duties under those regulations in respect of such a workplace shall apply accordingly;

(b)   which is used for the first time after 30th June 2003 shall comply with the requirements of regulations 7 and 11 from the date that it is first used and the employer's duties under those regulations in respect of such a workplace shall apply accordingly.

(3)   If, after 30th June 2003, any modification, extension or restructuring is undertaken in workplaces containing places where explosive atmospheres may occur, the employer shall take the necessary steps to ensure that the modification, extension or restructuring complies with the requirements of regulations 7 and 11 and the employer's duties under those regulations and in respect of such a modification, extension or restructuring shall apply accordingly.

(4)   Notwithstanding the amendment made to section 2(1) of the Petroleum (Consolidation) Act 1928[a] (provisions as to licences) made by regulation 15(1) and paragraph 2(1) and (2) of Schedule 6, a petroleum-spirit licence applying in any harbour which was granted by a harbour authority pursuant to section 2 of that Act and which is in force immediately before the date of the coming into force of regulation 15(1) and paragraph 2(1) and (2) of Schedule 6 shall continue in force in accordance with such conditions as were attached to it before that date, except that, where it makes provision for the renewal of the licence by the harbour authority, it shall have effect as if it provided for its renewal by the licensing authority under section 2(1)(a) or (c) of that Act for the area in which the harbour is situated; and any application for renewal made to the harbour authority before that date and not determined at that date shall have effect as if it had been made to that licensing authority.

(a) 1928 c.32. Section 2(1) is amended by the Local Government Act 1972 (c.70) section 251 and Schedule 29, Part II paragraph 32, by the Local Government Act 1985 (c.51) section 37 and Schedule II, paragraph 4, by the Local Government (Wales) Act 1994 (c.19) Section 22(3) and Schedule 9 paragraph 2 and by S.I. 1995/2923

(5) Notwithstanding the repeal of section 9 of the Petroleum (Consolidation) Act 1928 (byelaws as to loading, conveyance and landing of petroleum-spirit in and upon canals) by regulation 16(1) and Part 1 of Schedule 7, byelaws made or having effect under that section in force immediately before the date of the coming into force of regulation 16(1) and Part 1 of Schedule 7 shall continue in force.

337 Regulation 17 sets out the coming into force arrangements for regulations 7 and 11 as they apply to work equipment and protective systems, and workplaces. Tables 1 and 2 below summarise the arrangements for workplaces in use on or before 30 June 2003 and for workplaces used for the first time after this date.

Work equipment and protective systems first made available after 30 June 2003

338 Where equipment etc is installed in an explosive atmosphere after 30 June 2003, and it has not previously been used or placed on the market in the EU, it must be selected in accordance with the criteria set out in Schedule 3 - ie it must be selected on the basis of the categories of equipment in Schedule 4 of EPS[18] (unless the risk assessment finds otherwise).

339 EPS Regulations[19] which implement Directive 94/9/EC[18] (which was preceded by various other EEC Directives[a] on electrical equipment for use in potentially explosive atmospheres), apply to both electrical and mechanical equipment and protective systems intended for use in a potentially explosive atmosphere. Although 'responsible persons' have been able to place such equipment on the European market since 1 March 1996, the requirements of the EPS Regulations became mandatory for all such equipment and protective systems placed on the market or put into service in the EU for the first time after 30 June 2003.

340 Equipment intended for use in potentially explosive atmospheres that has been shown to meet the essential health and safety requirements of EPS[18] will carry the explosion protection symbol 'Ex' in a hexagon. Any intention to install such equipment etc after 30 June 2003 will require the employer to classify and zone the workplace.

Work equipment in use or made available on or before 30 June 2003

341 Any equipment or protective systems for use in a place where an explosive atmosphere may occur which:

(a) has previously been used or was being used in the workplace on or before 30 June 2003; or

(b) was available for use in the workplace on or before 30 June 2003 (eg on the shelf as spares)

may continue to be used, or may be brought into use for the first time, provided that it is safe to do so. Such equipment does not have to comply with the EPS Regulations[18] provided it does not need any substantial modification for installation.

(a) Council Directive 76/117/EEC on the Approximation of the Laws of the Member States Concerning Electrical Equipment for Use in Potentially Explosive Atmospheres; and Council Directive 79/196/EEC on the Approximation of the Laws of the Member States Concerning Electrical Equipment for Use in Potentially Explosive Atmosphere Concerning Certain Types of Protection (as last amended by Council Directive 90/487/EEC, Commission Directive 94/26/EC and Commission Directive 97/53/EC). These Directives were repealed on 1 July 2003.

342 Equipment in use on or before 30 June 2003 or available for use before or on that date that met the requirements of the Directives referred to in paragraph 339, can be assumed to be suitable for use in an explosive atmosphere as far as electrical hazards are concerned, provided that the equipment has not been modified and has been properly maintained. Equipment will also need to be suitable for use in an explosive atmosphere as far as its non-electrical hazards are concerned, for example where hot surfaces or friction could create a source of ignition.

Spare parts at existing facilities

343 Many employers keep a stock of spare parts of key items of equipment. Spare parts can be very simple items, that have no autonomous function, and are not EPS[18] equipment, but do contribute to safety, eg seals and gaskets. In other cases, spares may be complete items that are clearly equipment within the terms of the EPS Regulations, eg an electric motor, or an item of instrumentation. The EPS Regulations allow equipment at user premises or within the distribution chain, made before 30 June 2003 and complying with earlier legislation, to be brought into service after 1 July 2003.

344 DSEAR however, draws a distinction between a modification or extension to a workplace, and a workplace, which is simply maintained. If a workplace is significantly modified, extended or restructured, any new equipment provided should conform to the requirements of the EPS Regulations.[18]

345 During maintenance, if equipment or part of equipment is simply replaced by a spare that is essentially identical no new hazards should arise, no new risk assessment is needed, and spares that were in stock from before 30 June 2003 may be provided. However, if the employer has become aware of a safety risk associated with the part to be replaced, a new risk assessment may be needed, and a simple 'like for like' spare part may not be acceptable.

Workplaces already in use on or before 30 June 2003

346 Where a workplace was already in use on or before 30 June 2003, regulation 17(2) requires the employer to apply the provisions of regulations 7 and 11 by 30 June 2006. This allows a three-year transitional period during which time the employer should take steps to:

(a)   classify the workplace into hazardous and non-hazardous places, and further classify hazardous places into zones (regulation 7(1)). This means that the workplace may be classified into zones even though it may not at that time contain any equipment that has been selected on the basis of the categories set out in Schedule 4 of the EPS Regulations;[18]

(b)   mark hazardous places with a sign, where necessary (regulation 7(3));

(c)   provide appropriate work clothing (regulation 7(5)); and

(d)   where the workplace is shared, coordinate the implementation of measures required by these Regulations (regulation 11).

347 The employer must comply with all other requirements of these Regulations, insofar as they apply to the workplace, from the date they come into force.

348 During the three-year transitional period, the employer should review the assessment required by regulation 5(1) to ensure that it takes account of risks from explosive atmospheres, and identify where further action is necessary to comply with regulations 7 and 11. The timing of the review should be such that it allows sufficient time to introduce any necessary changes by 30 June 2006. The assessment should be reviewed again when the changes have been made to ensure that the requirements of regulations 7 and 11 have been fully met. The record of the assessment should be updated to show the information required by regulation 5(4).

349 The transitional arrangements are specific to the workplace and do not affect requirements pursuant to regulations 7(2) and 17(1) concerning equipment and protective systems.

Workplaces used for the first time after 30 June 2003

350 Where an employer brings a workplace into use for the first time after 30 June 2003, and that workplace contains places where explosive atmospheres may occur, regulations 7 and 11 apply in full, as appropriate and in addition to other requirements in these Regulations, from the date the workplace is first used.

Modifications to workplaces after 30 June 2003

351 If an employer carries out, after 30 June 2003, any modification, extension or restructuring of a workplace in which explosive atmospheres may occur, the area of the workplace affected by the modification, etc must comply with all of the requirements of these Regulations at the time the affected area is brought back into use. Further guidance on the transitional arrangements is given in the tables below.

Table 1 – Arrangements for workplaces in use on or before 30 June 2003

	When	Action
Equipment and protective systems already in use/available at the workplace	Immediately	Review equipment/protective systems against risk assessment requirements in regulation 5 of DSEAR. Equipment/protective systems at the workplace can continue to be used provided that the assessment indicates it is safe to do so.
Equipment and protective systems available for first time use after 30 June 2003	After 30 June 2003	Select equipment/protective systems that are new or available for the first time after this date in accordance with regulation 7(2)/Schedule 3 of DSEAR and the essential health and safety requirements in the EPS Regulations.[18] The place in which the equipment is to be located or used must be classified and zoned in accordance with regulation 7(1) of DSEAR if this has not yet been done during the transitional period for workplaces provided for in regulation 17(2)(a) of DSEAR.
Classification and zoning of hazardous areas	By 30 June 2006	Classify places into hazardous and non-hazardous places and zone hazardous places in accordance with regulation 7(1) of DSEAR. However, places may need to be classified before this date if equipment available for the first time after 30 June 2003 is to be used there.
Modifications etc to workplaces	After 30 June 2003	Ensure that any modification etc made to areas of the workplace that may contain an explosive atmosphere meets the requirements of regulations 7 and 11 of DSEAR from the date of the modification.
Marking hazardous places	By 30 June 2006	Provide any signs required by regulation 7(3)/Schedule 4 of DSEAR. If the part of the workplace to be marked is modified, etc after 30 June 2003, but before 30 June 2006, regulation 17(3) of DSEAR requires that signs are provided from the date of the modification.
Provision of work clothing	By 30 June 2006	Provide antistatic work clothing as required by regulation 7(5) of DSEAR. However, if the part of the workplace in which it is to be worn is modified, etc before this date it should be provided from the date of the modification.
Co-ordination of explosion protection measures	By 30 June 2006	Co-ordinate any measures required by regulation 11 of DSEAR and, as required by regulation 5(4) of DSEAR, record the aim of the co-ordination in the risk assessment. However, if part of the workplace is modified etc before 30 June 2006, the co-ordination requirements in respect of that part apply from the date of the modification.

Table 2 – Arrangements for workplaces used for the first time after 30 June 2003

	When	Action
Equipment and protective systems	Immediately	Select equipment or protective systems etc in accordance with regulation 7(2)/Schedule 3 of DSEAR and Schedule 4 of the EPS Regulations.[18]
Classification and zoning of hazardous areas	Immediately	Classify places into hazardous and non-hazardous places and zone hazardous places in accordance with regulation 7(1) of DSEAR.
Modifications etc to workplaces	When modification is made	Ensure that any modifications etc made to areas of the workplace that may contain an explosive atmosphere meet the requirements of regulations 7(1), 7(3), 7(5) and 11 of DSEAR from the date of the modification.
Marking hazardous places	Immediately	Provide any signs required by regulation 7(3)/Schedule 4 of DSEAR.
Verification of explosion safety	Before workplace is used for the first time	Ensure that the overall explosion safety of the workplace is verified by someone who is competent to do so as required by regulation 7(4) of DSEAR.
Provision of work clothing	Immediately	Provide antistatic work clothing as required by regulation 7(5) of DSEAR.
Co-ordination of explosion protection measures	Immediately	Co-ordinate any measures required by regulation 11 of DSEAR.

Petrol legislation

352   Regulation 17 also sets out transitional provisions for certain amendments to petrol legislation affecting harbour authorities and canal companies.

353   Harbour authorities can no longer issue petroleum licences (see paragraph 385 below) but any licences they may have issued, and any conditions attached to them, remain in force.

354   Canal companies can no longer introduce byelaws to control the carriage of petrol on their canals (see guidance on Schedule 7, paragraph 384) but any byelaws already in force continue in force.

General safety measures

Regulation 6(8)

1   *The following measures are those specified for the purposes of regulation 6(8).*

Workplace and work processes

2   *Ensuring that the workplace is designed, constructed and maintained so as to reduce risk.*

3   *Designing, constructing, assembling, installing, providing and using suitable work processes so as to reduce risk.*

4   *Maintaining work processes in an efficient state, in efficient working order and in good repair.*

5   *Ensuring that equipment and protective systems meet the following requirements -*

(a)   *where power failure can give rise to the spread of additional risk, equipment and protective systems must be able to be maintained in a safe state of operation independently of the rest of the plant in the event of power failure;*

(b)   *means for manual override must be possible, operated by employees competent to do so, for shutting down equipment and protective systems incorporated within automatic processes which deviate from the intended operating conditions, provided that the provision or use of such means does not compromise safety;*

(c)   *on operation of emergency shutdown, accumulated energy must be dissipated as quickly and as safely as possible or isolated so that it no longer constitutes a hazard; and*

(d)   *necessary measures must be taken to prevent confusion between connecting devices.*

Organisational measures

6   *The application of appropriate systems of work including -*

(a)   *the issuing of written instructions for the carrying out of the work; and*

(b)   *a system of permits to work with such permits being issued by a person with responsibility for this function prior to the commencement of the work concerned,*

where the work is carried out in hazardous places or involves hazardous activities.

Workplace and work processes

355   Schedule 1 sets out general safety measures that all employers should take to reduce risks from dangerous substances. The Schedule applies in addition to the specific requirements in regulation 7 that apply to equipment and protective systems for use in potentially explosive atmospheres. For employers who are not subject to regulation 7 (by virtue of regulation 3(2)), the Schedule provides the main means to reduce risks from dangerous substances and explosive atmospheres.

356 Work processes are defined widely in DSEAR (see regulation 2) and essentially relate to the 'hardware' used in workplaces where processing of dangerous substances takes place or where dangerous substances or explosive atmospheres are or are likely to be present. The requirements of Schedule 1 are to be applied so far as is reasonably practicable and subject to the measures being consistent with the risk assessment and appropriate to the nature of the activity or operation concerned.

357 Regulation 6(8) and Schedule 1 require employers, so far as is reasonably practicable, to ensure, among other matters, that work processes should be designed, constructed, assembled, installed, used and maintained in such a way as to reduce risk. This requirement relates not only to preventing sources of ignition, but to any other safety measures necessary to ensure that fires and explosions are prevented in the workplace.

358 For example, safety related control or protection systems for plant handling dangerous substances should be designed, integrated, used and maintained so that they have a sufficiently low likelihood of failure, or maloperation, leading to the release of dangerous substances into the workplace. That, in turn, will require the hardware and software in the instrumentation systems to be designed so that it can provide the required level of safe integrity.

359 This general requirement on the safety of work processes is therefore similar to the general duties under section 2 of HSW Act to provide and maintain machinery, equipment and plant that is, so far as is reasonably practicable, safe, and to the requirements of PUWER.[20]

360 Employers should use the results of the risk assessment required by regulation 5 to determine the suitability of the work process for its intended use. The following matters should be taken into account:

(a) the temperature and pressure under which it will operate, and the extent and speed with which these may change during operation. The combined effect of both temperature and pressure should also be considered;

(b) the ability of the work process to withstand the process or activity without risk of failure, including its life expectancy and inspection and maintenance requirements;

(c) the suitability of the construction materials and protective systems, so as to ensure:

- compatibility with other parts of the activity or process and the dangerous substances involved;

- resistance to internal and external corrosion that could result in failure;

- the ability to withstand brief exposure to fire;

(d) where it will be installed, operated, or used in an explosive atmosphere that it meets the specific requirements arising from the duties under regulation 7, where these apply; and

(e) in the case of a protective system, that it will be sufficient to deal with the likely size and spread of a fire, explosion or similar energetic event, taking into account the equipment to which it is attached.

361 For the purpose of this requirement work processes are intended to include 'equipment' defined in regulation 3(2) of EPS,[18] and 'work equipment' within the meaning of regulation 2(1) of PUWER.[20]

362 'Protective systems' are systems that are intended to stop a fire, explosion, or similar energetic event, or to limit its spread. They include such things as flame arresters, pressure relief (venting) systems, and suppression systems. Harmonised standards for many types of protective systems are being developed.

363 'Connecting devices' connect together pieces of equipment, apparatus etc and include items such as coupling devices or pipe connectors. Employers must take steps to ensure that incorrect connections are not made if these could result, for example, in the mixing of incompatible dangerous substances, or the use of unsuitable equipment. Many such devices are already manufactured in such a way as to prevent incorrect connection. However, where it would be possible to make unsafe connections further measures may be necessary, such as the use of labels, colour-coding etc. To avoid errors or confusion, the employer must also ensure that employees receive training, information and instruction in accordance with regulation 9 in respect of any such measures.

364 More detailed guidance on the design of work processes is contained in the ACOP for DSEAR on *Design of plant, equipment and process areas.*[2]

365 The Regulations also place a general duty on employers to provide a workplace that is suitable for the storage and/or use of dangerous substances. The risk assessment will determine what design features are needed in the workplace to reduce risk. Examples of precautions that may be required include: ventilation openings, fire resisting walls, explosion relief panels, etc.

366 The ACOP and guidance to the Workplace (Health, Safety and Welfare) Regulations 1992[42] and the publication *Fire safety. An employer's guide*[67] also provide useful advice on the design of workplaces for safety.

367 The Regulations also require the chosen design features in the workplace to be maintained so as to ensure safety.

Equipment and protective systems

368 The risk assessment required by regulation 5(1) should take into account the circumstances of the work, including the operating conditions that are necessary for an activity to maintain the safe operation of a process or work activity.

369 As part of this, the employer should consider the consequences of a power failure or the deviation of a process from its normal operating conditions. It may be sufficient to ensure that the plant can be shut down manually; alternatively control systems should maintain safety if loss of power could lead to the unintentional release of a dangerous substance.

370 The employer should ensure that arrangements are in place to ensure that equipment and/or protective systems remain safe in the event of a power failure and that the removal of the original source of power will not lead, for example, to over-pressurisation, over-filling, or temperatures that are too low or too high. This is particularly important for processes that involve chemically unstable substances or exothermic reactions where the failure of the equipment or protective system could lead to a runaway reaction.

371 Where it is safe to do so, the employer should also be able to shut down an automatic process through a manual override system before it reaches its safe operating limit. On complex systems, it may be more appropriate to provide a back-up power supply that will provide power for sufficient time to shut the plant safely.

372 In the event of such a shut down any energy that has been created by the process must be either dispersed quickly and safely, for example through a suitable discharge system, or safely isolated. For example, a cooling system to a reactor may need to operate for a period following loss of power, or machinery brakes may need to be operated by hand.

373 The employer should ensure that employees authorised to take override action receive the information, instruction and training in accordance with regulation 9 necessary to enable them to determine when override action is appropriate and be competent to perform their duties correctly and with due regard for safety.

Organisational matters

374 Regulation 6(8) and the Schedule require that the employer applies appropriate systems of work.

375 There are similar requirements in section 2 of the HSW Act and in the MHSW Regulations.[11] These requirements point to the need for properly applied safety management systems to control and mitigate the risk of fire and explosion. This involves at a general level:

(a) planning;

(b) organisation;

(c) control;

(d) monitoring;

(e) review.

376 Permits-to-work, written instructions, safety method statements, and similar procedural methods play an important part in organising and controlling work, particularly where these are high risk, and novel or unfamiliar, eg in non-routine maintenance activities.

377 Further information on safety management systems can be found in the HSE publication *Successful health and safety management*[85] and in the ACOP[61] to the MHSW Regulations.[11]

378 Information on permits-to-work, written instructions and safety method statements can be found in the ACOP to DSEAR on *Safe maintenance, repair and cleaning procedures*.[5]

Classification of places where explosive atmospheres may occur

Regulation 7(1)
(which substantially reproduces the provisions of Annex I of Council Directive 99/92/EC[(a)])

1   Places where explosive atmospheres may occur

A place in which an explosive atmosphere may occur in such quantities as to require special precautions to protect the health and safety of the workers concerned is deemed to be hazardous within the meaning of these Regulations.

A place in which an explosive atmosphere is not expected to occur in such quantities as to require special precautions is deemed to be non-hazardous within the meaning of these Regulations.

2   Classification of hazardous places

Hazardous places are classified in terms of zones on the basis of the frequency and duration of the occurrence of an explosive atmosphere.

Zone 0

A place in which an explosive atmosphere consisting of a mixture with air of dangerous substances in the form of gas, vapour or mist is present continuously or for long periods or frequently.

Zone 1

A place in which an explosive atmosphere consisting of a mixture with air of dangerous substances in the form of gas, vapour or mist is likely to occur in normal operation occasionally.

Zone 2

A place in which an explosive atmosphere consisting of a mixture with air of dangerous substances in the form of gas, vapour or mist is not likely to occur in normal operation but, if it does occur, will persist for a short period only.

Zone 20

A place in which an explosive atmosphere in the form of a cloud of combustible dust in air is present continuously, or for long periods or frequently.

Zone 21

A place in which an explosive atmosphere in the form of a cloud of combustible dust in air is likely to occur in normal operation occasionally.

Zone 22

A place in which an explosive atmosphere in the form of a cloud of combustible dust in air is not likely to occur in normal operation but, if it does occur, will persist for a short period only.

Notes:

1   Layers, deposits and heaps of combustible dust must be considered as any other source which can form an explosive atmosphere.

2   "Normal operation" means the situation when installations are used within their design parameters.

(a) OJ No. L23, 28.1.00, p.57

Criteria for the selection of equipment and protective systems

Regulation 7(2)

1   *Equipment and protective systems for all places in which explosive atmospheres may occur must be selected on the basis of the requirements set out in the Equipment and Protective Systems Intended for Use in Potentially Explosive Atmospheres Regulations 1996[a] unless the risk assessment finds otherwise.*

2   *In particular, the following categories of equipment must be used in the zones indicated, provided they are suitable for gases, vapours, mists, dusts or mists and dusts, as appropriate:*

-     *in zone 0 or zone 20, category 1 equipment,*

-     *in zone 1 or zone 21, category 1 or 2 equipment,*

-     *in zone 2 or zone 22, category 1, 2 or 3 equipment.*

3   *For the purposes of this Schedule and regulations 7(2) and 17(1) -*

(a)   *"equipment" means machines, apparatus, fixed or mobile devices, control components and instrumentation thereof and detection or prevention systems which, separately or jointly, are intended for the generation, transfer, storage, measurement, control and conversion of energy and the processing of material, as the case may be, and which are capable of causing an explosion through their own potential sources of ignition;*

(b)   *"protective systems" means devices other than components of equipment which are intended to halt incipient explosions immediately or limit the effective range of an explosion or both, as the case may be, and which systems are separately placed on the market for use as autonomous systems;*

(c)   *"devices" means safety devices, controlling devices and regulating devices intended for use outside potentially explosive atmospheres but required for or contributing to the safe functioning of equipment and protective systems with respect to the risks of explosion;*

(d)   *"component" means any item essential to the safe functioning of equipment and protective systems but with no autonomous function; and*

(e)   *"potentially explosive atmosphere" means an atmosphere which could become explosive due to local and operational conditions.*

(a) S.I. 1996/192, amended by S.I. 2001/3766

Warning sign for places where explosive atmospheres may occur

Regulation 7(3)
(which substantially reproduces the provisions of Annex III of Council Directive 99/92/EC)

Distinctive features:

    (a)   triangular shape;

    (b)   black letters on a yellow background with black edging (the yellow part to take up at least 50% of the area of the sign).

Legislation concerned with the marking of containers and pipes

Regulation 10

The Classification and Labelling of Explosives Regulations 1983 (S.I. 1983/1140).

The Chemicals (Hazard Information and Packaging for Supply) Regulations 2002 (S.I.2002/1689).

The Health and Safety (Safety Signs and Signals) Regulations 1996 (S.I.1996/341).

The Radioactive Material (Road Transport) (Great Britain) Regulations 1996 (S.I.1996/1350).

The Carriage of Dangerous Goods by Rail Regulations 1996 (S.I.1996/2089).

The Packaging, Labelling and Carriage of Radioactive Material by Rail Regulations 1996 (S.I.1996/2090).

The Carriage of Dangerous Goods (Classification, Packaging and Labelling) and Use of Transportable Pressure Receptacles Regulations 1996 (S.I.1996/2092).

The Carriage of Explosives by Road Regulations 1996 (S.I.1996/2093).

The Carriage of Dangerous Goods by Road Regulations 1996 (S.I.1996/2095).

The Good Laboratory Practice Regulations 1997 (S.I.1997/654).

Amendments

Regulation 15

Part 1

379 The amendments have been introduced to remove petroleum licensing and associated legislation from all workplace premises not involved in petrol dispensing. DSEAR has introduced modern goal-setting legislation to prevent fire and explosion risks from flammable substances and the prescriptive controls of petrol licensing are no longer appropriate to such places.

380 However, all parts of premises where dispensing of petrol takes place remain subject to licensing. Non-workplace premises also continue to be licensed. These are domestic premises plus other premises where there is no employment, including self-employment, but which are not domestic premises eg a boat club with a clubhouse where some petrol is kept but if there are no employees would not be work premises.

381 All other amendments in Part 1 of Schedule 6 are consequential on this change, except for the amendments to the Celluloid and Cinematic Film Act 1922[86] and the FPWR.[13]

    1   *In section 2 of the Celluloid and Cinematograph Film Act 1922[a] (purposes to which Act applies), after paragraph (iii) of the proviso insert*

"and

(iv) the provisions of this Act shall not apply to a workplace within the meaning of the Fire Precautions (Workplace) Regulations 1997[b].".

(a) 1922 c.35. Section 2 is amended by the Cinemas Act 1985 (c.13), section 24(1) and Schedule 2, paragraph 1 and S.I. 1992/1811
(b) S.I. 1997/1840, amended by S.I. 1999/1877 and 1999/3242

382 The Celluloid and Cinematograph Film Act 1922[86] has been amended so that it no longer has effect in relation to workplaces as defined by the Fire Precautions (Workplace) Regulations 1997.[13] The Act still applies to celluloid and cinematograph film at non-workplaces (eg domestic premises) and the self-employed.

    2   *(1)   The Petroleum (Consolidation) Act 1928[c] is amended as follows.*

    (2)   In section 2 (provisions as to licences), omit the proviso to subsection (1) (special provision for harbours).

(c) 1928 c.32. Section 2(1) is amended by the Local Government Act 1972 (c.70) section 251 and Schedule 29, Part II paragraph 32, by the Local Government Act 1985 (c.51) section 37 and Schedule II paragraph 4 and by the Local Government (Wales) Act 1994 (c.19) section 22(3) and Schedule 9 paragraph 2; section 18 is amended by S.I. 1974/1942, 1986/1951 and 1992/743; section 23 is amended by the Statute Law (Repeals) Act 1993 (c.50) and by S.I. 1974/1942, 1992/1811, 1993/1746 and 1994/3247; section 25A is inserted by S.I. 1999/743

383 The power of harbour authorities to issue petroleum licences has been removed. It will now fall instead to the relevant local authority as the petroleum licensing authority (PLA) to issue any petroleum licences required in harbour areas.

(3)   Omit section 9 (byelaws as to loading, conveyance and landing of petroleum-spirit in and upon canals) and section 17 (powers of officers as to testing petroleum-spirit).

384   The power of canal companies to make byelaws has been removed as they have sufficient powers, other than making byelaws, available to them.

385   Section 17 previously provided for Petroleum Licensing Officers to take samples of petroleum but the HSW Act gives alternative powers so the PCA[22] power has been repealed.

(4)   In section 18 (warrants to search for and seize petroleum-spirit), for subsection (4) substitute -

"(4)   This section does not apply to -

(a)   a workplace within the meaning of the Dangerous Substances and Explosive Atmospheres Regulations 2002 used, or intended for use, for the dispensing of petroleum-spirit, or

(b)   carriage to which the Carriage of Dangerous Goods by Road Regulations 1996[(a)] apply.".

(a) S.I. 1996/2095, amended by S.I. 1998/2885, 1999/257, 1999/303 and 2001/1426

386   HSW Act provides adequate powers to PLAs in relation to workplaces so the PCA[22] section 18 powers are now only needed at non-workplaces. The amendment to section 25A (see paragraph 388 below) disapplies the whole of PCA, including section 18, from all workplaces covered by DSEAR except for premises where petrol is dispensed so the only other disapplications required are for premises where petrol is dispensed and for carriage.

(5)   In section 23 (interpretation) -

(a)   after the definition of "Contravention" insert-

""the Directive" means Commission Directive 92/69 EEC[(b)] adapting to technical progress for the seventeenth time Council Directive 67/548/EEC[(c)] on the approximation of laws, regulations and administrative provisions relating to the classification, packaging and labelling of dangerous substances:

"Dispensing" means manual or electrical pumping of petroleum-spirit from a storage tank into the fuel tank for an internal combustion engine, whether for the purposes of sale or not:"; and

(b)   for the definition of "Petroleum-spirit" substitute -

""Petroleum-spirit" means petroleum which, when tested in accordance with Part A.9. of the Annex to the Directive, has a flash point (as defined in that Part) of less than 21°C:".

(6)   Re-number section 25A[(d)] (places to which Act does not apply) as subsection (1) and insert at the end

(b) OJ No. L383, 29.12.92, p.113
(c) OJ No. 196, 16.8.67, p.1
(d) Section 25A was inserted by S.I. 1999/743

"or

(c)   any workplace within the meaning of the Dangerous Substances and Explosive Atmospheres Regulations 2002, apart from a workplace used, or intended for use, for dispensing petroleum-spirit.

(2)   For the purposes of subsection (1)(c), any part of a workplace where petroleum-spirit is kept other than for dispensing is not to be regarded as used, or intended for use, for dispensing petroleum-spirit.".

387 Dispensing is defined so as to exclude decanting of petrol from a portable container, eg a jerry can.

388 The key change implemented by Schedule 6 is the removal of petroleum licensing from all workplace storage of petrol except where it is kept in connection with dispensing. This is achieved by disapplying PCA[22] from all premises covered by DSEAR except in connection with dispensing. As DSEAR applies only to workplaces it automatically excludes non-workplace premises (mainly domestic) from the disapplication and the overall effect is that only petrol dispensing activities and non-workplace premises are subject to licensing. Where there is both dispensing and non-dispensing storage on the same premises then only the petrol kept for dispensing continues to be licensed - the petrol kept for other purposes does not need a licence.

389 PCA,[22] and any other legislation that derives from PCA, continues to apply to all petrol dispensing activities and to non-workplace premises.

3   (1)   The Petroleum-Spirit (Motor Vehicles 'etc') Regulations 1929[a] are amended as follows.

(2)   For regulation 2 (keeping of petroleum-spirit), substitute -

"2   (1)   Subject to paragraph (2), the petroleum-spirit shall not be kept otherwise than in metal vessels so constructed and maintained in such a condition as -

(a)   to be reasonably secure against breakage; and

(b)   to prevent the leakage of any liquid or vapour therefrom.

(2)   Where the vessel in which the petroleum-spirit is to be kept is a fuel tank for an internal combustion engine, the requirement in paragraph (1) that the vessel be made of metal shall not apply.".

(a) S.I. 1929/952, amended by S.I 1979/427, 1982/630, 1992/1811 and 1999/743; the last mentioned instrument inserted regulation 15A(a) and (b)

390 This amendment to regulation 2 of the Petroleum-Spirit (Motor Vehicles etc) Regulations 1929[87] brings these Regulations into line with the Recreational Craft Directive,[88] which allows plastic fuel tanks for internal combustion engines on small boats. The amendment also allows for plastic fuel tanks in vehicles. Strictly, plastic fuel tanks were not prohibited prior to this amendment but a petroleum licence would have been required.

(3)   In regulation 7, insert at the beginning of paragraph (1) "Subject to paragraph (3) below," and after paragraph (2) insert -

"(3)   The disapplication from the requirements of paragraph (1) above in respect of a fuel tank for an internal combustion engine shall only apply to a fuel

Schedule 6

tank which remains connected to the fuel system of the internal combustion engine it is serving in the way it would ordinarily be so connected when that engine is running.".

Guidance

391   This amendment to regulation 7 of the Petroleum-Spirit (Motor Vehicles etc) Regulations 1929[87] prevents fuel tanks from being stored separately from the vehicle or vessel to which they belong and prevents spare fuel tanks being stored without a licence.

Schedule 6

(4)   In regulation 15A (disapplication), omit "and" at the end of paragraph (a) and insert after paragraph (b) -

"or

(c)   any workplace within the meaning of the Dangerous Substances and Explosive Atmospheres Regulations 2002.".

Guidance

392   This amendment disapplies the Petroleum-Spirit (Motor Vehicles etc) Regulations 1929[87] from all workplace premises covered by DSEAR including petrol filling stations. They now only apply to non-workplaces (mainly domestic premises).

Schedule 6

4   The Petroleum (Liquid Methane) Order 1957[(a)] is amended by the insertion at the end of the Schedule (provisions of the Petroleum (Consolidation) Act 1928 not applied to liquid methane), of "Section 25A(1)(c) and (2)".

(a) S.I. 1957/859

Guidance

393   This amendment to the Liquid Methane Order ensures that liquid methane remains subject to PCA[22] at all workplaces, including retail petrol filling stations, except COMAH[26] and Notification of Installations Handling Hazardous Substances Regulations 1982 (NIHHS)[89] sites.

394   The Petroleum (Liquid Methane) Order 1957[90] requires liquid methane to be treated administratively as if it was petrol and thus it requires a licence. Although liquid methane is subject to DSEAR, which will provide adequate control over its storage and use, it will remain subject to PCA[22] until guidance has been prepared to ensure that adequate standards are maintained.

395   PCA,[22] and therefore the order, has not applied to workplaces subject to COMAH[26] and NIHHS[89] since the insertion into PCA[22] of sections 25A(a) and (b) by the COMAH[26] Regulations. DSEAR has further amended PCA section 25A by adding section 25A(1)(c) and (2) which disapply PCA[22] from all workplace storage of petrol except where it is kept for dispensing (see paragraph 388 above).

Schedule 6

5   (1) The Petroleum (Consolidation) Act 1928 (Enforcement) Regulations 1979[(b)] are amended as follows:

(2)   In regulation 1(2) (citation, commencement and interpretation), after the definition of "the 1974 Act" insert -

""the Directive" means Commission Directive 92/69 EEC[(c)] adapting to technical progress for the seventeenth time Council Directive 67/548/EEC[(d)] on the approximation of laws, regulations and administrative provisions relating to the classification, packaging and labelling of dangerous substances;

(b) S.I. 1979/427, amended by S.I. 1981/1059, 1982/630 and 1986/1951
(c) OJ No. L383, 29.12.92, p. 113
(d) OJ No. 196, 16.8.67, p.1

"dispensing" means manual or electrical pumping of petroleum-spirit from a storage tank into the fuel tank for an internal combustion engine, whether for the purposes of sale or not, and "dispenser" shall be construed accordingly;

"Her Majesty's Forces" means any of the naval, military or air forces of the Crown, whether raised inside or outside the United Kingdom and whether any such force is a regular, auxiliary or reserve force, and includes any civilian employed by those forces;

"non-retail petroleum filling station" means premises used, or intended for use, for dispensing petroleum-spirit for use in motor vehicles, ships or aircraft, but it does not include any retail petroleum filling station;

"petroleum-spirit" means petroleum which, when tested in accordance with Part A.9. of the Annex to the Directive has a flash point (as defined in that Part) of less than 21°C ;

"retail petroleum filling station" means premises used, or intended for use, for dispensing petroleum-spirit to the public for use in motor vehicles, ships or aircraft by way of sale;

"ship" includes every description of vessel used in navigation propelled by means of an internal combustion engine and any reference to "ship" in these Regulations includes a reference to hovercraft; and

"vehicle fuel" means petroleum-spirit or any other substance which provides the power in an internal-combustion engine in a motor vehicle, ship or aircraft".

396 This amendment introduces a number of necessary definitions.

(3)   In regulation 2(1) (enforcing authorities) -

(a)   for "Subject to paragraphs (2) and (3)" substitute "Subject to paragraphs (2) to (4)";

(b)   omit subparagraph (a)(i), (iii) and (iv);

397 The Calcium Carbide Orders of 1929[91] and 1947[92] and the Compressed Gases Order[93] have been revoked (see paragraph 409) so the references to those orders have been removed.

(c)   insert after subparagraph (c) -

"(d) the Dangerous Substances and Explosive Atmospheres Regulations 2002 -

(i)   in so far as they apply to any activity relating to fuelling motor vehicles and ships with vehicle fuel, and fuelling aircraft with petroleum-spirit, at a retail petroleum filling station, including any vehicle fuel dispenser, other apparatus or storage tank for storing vehicle fuel used thereat in connection with the fuelling concerned of those respective kinds of fuelling; and

(ii) in so far as they apply to any activity relating to fuelling motor vehicles, ships and aircraft with petroleum-spirit at a non-retail petroleum filling station, including any petroleum-spirit dispenser, other apparatus or storage tank for storing petroleum-spirit used thereat in connection with that fuelling."; and

(d) after paragraph (3), insert -

"(4) Nothing in paragraph (1) (d) shall apply to -

(a) Her Majesty's Forces;

(b) any establishment to which the Control of Major Accident Hazards Regulations 1999[a] apply by virtue of regulation 3 of those Regulations;

(c) any site in respect of which notification of an activity is required pursuant to regulation 3 of the Notification of Installations Handling Hazardous Substances Regulations 1982[b]; and

(d) any activity at a retail or a non-retail petroleum filling station connected with repairing motor vehicles, ships or aircraft or retailing goods other than, in relation to a retail petroleum filling station, vehicle fuel and, in relation to a non-retail petroleum filling station, petroleum-spirit.".

(a) S.I. 1999/743, amended by the Greater London Authority Act 1999 (c.29), section 328(7), and S.I. 1999/2597
(b) S.I. 1982/1357, amended by S.I. 1996/825

398 PLAs have been allocated responsibility for enforcing DSEAR at sites, which dispense petrol, but with certain limitations. At retail petrol filling stations the PLA enforces DSEAR in connection with petrol and any other vehicle fuels within the scope of DSEAR (liquefied petroleum gas (LPG), which is becoming more common, compressed natural gas (CNG) and liquefied natural gas (LNG) which are quite rare) but has no responsibility for such substances where they are not present for vehicle fuelling purposes eg LPG in cylinders. At non-retail petrol filling stations the PLA only enforces DSEAR in connection with petrol but no other vehicle fuels. The PLA has no DSEAR responsibility for sites where there is no petrol being dispensed eg sites that dispense only LPG. The PLA continues to be the enforcing agency as long as the site is used, or is intended to be used, for dispensing petrol. Thus, a filling station site which has temporarily closed, but which is intended to re-open or to be sold as a going concern, will continue to be enforced by the PLA. If the site closes completely and is to be demolished, then enforcement of the demolition activity passes to HSE.

399 The repair of vehicles or ships, including boats, containing fuel is covered by DSEAR but enforcement in connection with these activities is always the responsibility of the normal enforcing authority for the HSW Act at the premises, not the PLA.

6 (1) The Petroleum-Spirit (Plastic Containers) Regulations 1982[c] are amended as follows.

(2) In regulation 8 (disapplication), omit "and" at the end of paragraph (a) and insert at the end of paragraph (b)

"or

(c) any workplace within the meaning of the Dangerous Substances and Explosive Atmospheres Regulations 2002.".

(c) S.I. 1982/630, amended by S.I. 1999/743

400   The Petroleum-Spirit (Plastic Containers) Regulations 1982[94] have been disapplied from all workplace premises including retail petrol filling stations. They now only apply to non-workplace premises (mainly domestic premises). This means that there is no maximum size limit for plastic containers used for storing petrol at workplace premises and brings petrol into line with other highly flammable liquids (HFLs), which may be found in workplaces. Workplaces are, however, subject to DSEAR and the controls they impose including, where necessary, reducing the amounts of dangerous substances present so as to reduce the risk of fires and explosions. Petrol in the workplace is now treated like any other HFL.

401   The existing controls on plastic containers for petrol present in non-workplaces continue to apply. Workplaces include vehicles used for or in connection with work. These Regulations, including the limits on the size and number of plastic containers, which may be carried, continue to apply to vehicles not being used for or in connection with work.

7   *The Dangerous Substances in Harbour Areas Regulations 1987[(a)] are amended by the omission of "the Petroleum (Carbide of Calcium) Order 1929" in regulation 29 (application of Part VIII - storage of dangerous substances).*

(a) S.I. 1987/37, amended by S.I. 1993/1746, 1994/669, 1994/3247, 1996/2092, 1996/2095, 1997/2367, 1998/2885 and 1999/2029

402   The Calcium Carbide Order 1929[91] has been revoked (see paragraph 409) and reference to it has been removed from the Dangerous Substances in Harbour Areas Regulations 1987.[95]

8   *The Fire Precautions (Workplace) Regulations 1997[(b)] are amended by the insertion of "and regulations 1 to 6, 8, 9 and 11 of the Dangerous Substances and Explosive Atmospheres Regulations 2002," after "the 1999 Management Regulations" in paragraph (2)(b) of regulation 9 (disapplication).*

(b) S.I. 1997/1840, amended by S.I. 1999/1877 and 1999/3242

403   The FPW Regulations[13] are amended to avoid duplication with existing fire safety legislation (enforced by the fire authorities) and the requirements of DSEAR in relation to accidents and emergencies. This makes specific provisions of DSEAR (eg the risk assessment requirement) part of 'workplace fire precautions legislation'; which would have the effect of making the fire authorities the enforcing authority for those parts of DSEAR in relation to general fire safety (eg means of escape etc).

Part 2

9   *(1)   The Fire Certificates (Special Premises) Regulations 1976[(c)] are amended as follows.*

(2)   In paragraph 25 of Part III of Schedule 1 (premises for which a fire certificate is required), for the definition of "highly flammable liquid" substitute -

""highly flammable liquid" means any liquid, liquid solution, emulsion or suspension, other than aqueous ammonia, liquefied flammable gas, and liquefied petroleum gas, which -

(a)   when tested in accordance with Part A.9. of the Annex to the Directive

(c) S.I. 1976/2003, amended by S.I. 1985/1333, 1987/37 and 1992/1811

has a flash point (as defined in that Part) of less than 32°C except that, if the flash point determined by using one of the non-equilibrium methods referred to in that Part falls within the range 30°C to 34°C, that flash point shall be confirmed by the use of like apparatus using the appropriate equilibrium method referred to in that Part; and

(b) when tested at 50°C (within an accuracy of - 0 + 5°C) using the procedure referred to in Appendix B to the "Approved Requirements and test methods for the classification and packaging of dangerous goods for carriage"[a] with a heating time of 60 seconds supports combustion,

and for these purposes -

(i) "aqueous ammonia" means ammonia gas dissolved in water;

(ii) "the Directive" means Commission Directive 92/69 EEC[b] adapting to technical progress for the seventeenth time Council Directive 67/548/EEC[c] on the approximation of laws, regulations and administrative provisions relating to the classification, packaging and labelling of dangerous substances; and

(iii) "liquefied flammable gas" means any substance which at a temperature of 20°C and a pressure of 760 millimetres of mercury would be a flammable gas, but which is in liquid form as a result of the application of pressure refrigeration or both.".

10   The Carriage of Dangerous Goods by Road Regulations 1996[d] are amended by the substitution for regulation 20 (unloading of petrol at petroleum filling stations and certain other premises licensed for the keeping of petrol) of -

"Direct filling of fuel tanks with petrol from road tankers

20   (1) Neither the fuel tank for an internal combustion engine nor a portable container shall be filled or replenished with petrol direct from a road tanker conveying petrol in such circumstances that these Regulations apply to that conveyance.

(2)   Except in relation to Her Majesty's Forces, the enforcing authority for these Regulations and for sections 2 to 4 and sections 7 and 8 of the Health and Safety at Work etc Act 1974 in respect of such filling or replenishing with petrol as is referred to in paragraph (1) at any premises for which a petroleum-spirit licence authorising the keeping of petrol is required under the 1928 Act, shall be the petroleum licensing authority, even if the relevant tanker is on a road at the time of that filling or replenishing.

(3)   In this regulation -

(a) "the 1928 Act" means the Petroleum (Consolidation) Act 1928[e];

(b) "the Directive" means Commission Directive 92/69 EEC adapting to technical progress for the seventeenth time Council Directive 67/548/EEC on the approximation of laws, regulations and administrative provisions relating to the classification, packaging and labelling of dangerous substances;

(a) ISBN 0 7176 1221 X
(b) OJ No. L383, 29.12.92, p.113
(c) OJ No. 196, 16.8.67, p.1
(d) S.I. 1996/2095, amended by S.I. 1998/2885, 1999/257, 1999/303 and 2001/1426
(e) 1928 c.32

(c)   "Her Majesty's Forces" means any of the naval, military or air forces of the Crown, whether raised inside or outside the United Kingdom and whether any such force is a regular, auxiliary or reserve force, and includes any civilian employed by those forces;

(d)   "petrol" means petroleum-spirit intended for use as a fuel for an internal combustion engine;

(e)   "the petroleum licensing authority" means the local authority empowered to grant petroleum-spirit licences under the 1928 Act for the premises concerned;

(f)   "petroleum-spirit" means petroleum which, when tested in accordance with Part A.9. of the Annex to the Directive has a flash point (as defined in that Part) of less than 21 °C; and

(g)   "petroleum-spirit licence" means a licence authorising the keeping of petroleum-spirit granted by a local authority empowered under the 1928 Act to grant such a licence or by the Secretary of State or by the Health and Safety Executive.".

404   Schedule 12 of the CDG Regulations 1996,[29] which imposed controls on the unloading of petrol from road tankers, has been revoked and unloading of petrol from road tankers is now covered by an Approved Code of Practice, *Unloading petrol from road tankers*.[6]

405   Schedule 12 had the effect of prohibiting unloading petrol from a road tanker into anything other than a storage tank. The prohibition in the revised regulation 20 focuses on prohibiting unloading a road tanker into a vehicle fuel tank and applies everywhere that CDG[29] applies, including COMAH[26] and NIHHS[89] workplaces and sites storing more than 100 000 litres of petrol. The prohibition applies only to petrol and prohibits unloading into the fuel tank for any internal combustion engine, not just vehicles. However, because the prohibition applies only where CDG applies it should be read in conjunction with Schedule 2 of those Regulations (disapplications). In particular, most of the CDG Regulations[29] do not apply to tankers carrying petrol to fuel aircraft on aerodromes (which are defined in paragraph 10 of Schedule 2). In these situations, refuelling aircraft direct from a road tanker will continue to be permissible. The CDG Regulations do have provision for exemption certificates to be issued and HSE would consider any application for an exemption to this prohibition. Each case would be considered on its individual merits.

406   PLAs enforce the prohibition at all workplaces with a petroleum-spirit licence. At other workplaces the enforcing authority is HSE or the local authority as appropriate.

Repeal and revocation

Regulation 16

407   The repeals and revocations in Part 1 of Schedule 7 of the DSEAR Regulations came into force on 9 December 2002, those in Part 2 came into force on 5 May 2003.

Part 1

Repeal and revocation

Column 1	Column 2	Column 3
Title	*Reference*	*Extent of repeal*
The Petroleum (Consolidation) Act 1928	*c.32*	*The proviso to section 2(1).* *Section 9.* *Section 17.* *In section 25A, the word "and" at the end of paragraph (a).*
The Celluloid, etc Factories and Workshops Regulations 1921	*S.R. & O. 1921/1825*	*The whole Regulations.*
The Manufacture of Cinematograph Film Regulations 1928	*S.R. & O. 1928/82*	*The whole Regulations.*
The Petroleum (Carbide of Calcium) Order 1929	*S.R. & O. 1929/992*	*The whole Order.*
The Petroleum (Compressed Gases) Order 1930	*S.R. & O. 1930/34*	*The whole Order.*
The Cinematograph Film Stripping Regulations 1939	*S.R & O.1939/571*	*The whole Regulations.*
The Petroleum (Carbide of Calcium) Order 1947	*S. R. & O. 1947/1442*	*The whole Order.*

Petroleum (Consolidation) Act 1928

408   Section 9 of PCA[22] gave canal operating companies the power to introduce byelaws to control the carriage of petrol on their canals. These powers are no longer required, as the canal operating companies have adequate alternative powers to making byelaws, and this section has been repealed. Any byelaws already in existence remain in force (see paragraph 384).

Calcium carbide

409   The only significant commercial use of calcium carbide is for the manufacture of acetylene which is adequately controlled by various orders and regulations under the Explosives Act 1875[45] and DSEAR. The Calcium Carbide Orders[91/92] are, therefore, no longer required and have been revoked together with references to them.

Compressed gases

410   The Petroleum (Compressed Gases) Order 1930[93] mainly addressed the manner in which some gas cylinders were marked. These requirements are now adequately dealt with by the CHIP Regulations[34] and DSEAR, so the order has been revoked.

Part 2

Repeal and revocation

Column 1 *Title*	Column 2 *Reference*	Column 3 *Extent of repeal or revocation*
The Factories Act 1961	*c.34*	*Section 31.*
The Magnesium (Grinding of Castings and other Articles) Special Regulations 1946	*S.R. & O. 1946/2197*	*The whole Regulations.*
The Dry Cleaning Special Regulations 1949	*S.I. 1949/2224*	*The whole Regulations.*
The Factories (Testing of Aircraft Engines and Accessories) Special Regulations 1952	*S.I. 1952/1689*	*The whole Regulations.*
The Shipbuilding and Ship-repairing Regulations 1960[a]	*S.I. 1960/1932*	*Regulations 48 to 52,54 and 55 to 66.*
The Highly Flammable Liquids and Liquefied Petroleum Gases Regulations 1972	*S.I. 1972/917*	*The whole Regulations.*
The Abstract of Special Regulations (Highly Flammable Liquids and Liquefied Petroleum Gases) Regulations Order 1974	*S.I. 1974/1587*	*The whole Order.*
The Dry Cleaning (Metrication) Regulations 1983	*S.I. 1983/977*	*The whole Regulations.*
The Factories (Testing of Aircraft Engines and Accessories) (Metrication) Regulations 1983	*S.I. 1983/979*	*The whole Regulations.*
The Dangerous Substances in Harbour Area Regulations 1987	*S.I. 1987/37*	*Regulation 29(a).*
The Workplace (Health, Safety and Welfare) Regulations 1992	*S.I. 1992/3004*	*Regulation 6(3)(b).*
The Carriage of Dangerous Goods (Classification, Packaging and Labelling) and Use of Transportable Pressure Receptacles Regulations 1996	*S.I. 1996/2092*	*Regulation 22(b).*
The Carriage of Dangerous Goods by Road Regulations 1996	*S.I. 1996/2095*	*Schedule 12.*

(a) Regulations 48 to 52 and 54 were revoked by S.I. 1997/1713, regulation 9(2) and the Schedule, save insofar as they applied to the matters referred to in regulation 2(a) to (c) of S.I. 1997/1713

References

1   *The Dangerous Substances and Explosive Atmospheres Regulations 2002*
SI 2002/2776 The Stationery Office 2002 ISBN 0 11 042957 5

2   *Design of plant, equipment and workplaces. Dangerous Substances and
Explosive Atmospheres Regulations 2002. Approved Code of Practice and guidance*
L138 HSE Books 2003 ISBN 0 7176 2199 5

3   *Storage of dangerous substances. Dangerous Substances and Explosive
Atmospheres Regulations 2002. Approved Code of Practice and guidance*
L135 HSE Books 2003 ISBN 0 7176 2200 2

4   *Control and mitigation measures. Dangerous Substances and Explosive
Atmospheres Regulations 2002. Approved Code of Practice and guidance*
L136 HSE Books 2003 ISBN 0 7176 2201 0

5   *Safe maintenance, repair and cleaning procedures. Dangerous Substances and
Explosive Atmospheres Regulations 2002. Approved Code of Practice and guidance*
L137 HSE Books 2003 ISBN 0 7176 2202 9

6   *Unloading petrol from road tankers. Dangerous Substances and Explosive
Atmospheres Regulations 2002. Approved Code of Practice and guidance*
L133 HSE Books 2003 ISBN 0 7176 2197 9

7   *Fire and explosion: How safe is your workplace? A short guide to the
Dangerous Substances and Explosive Atmospheres Regulations* Leaflet INDG370
HSE Books 2002 (single copy free or priced packs of 5 ISBN 0 7176 2589 3)

8   *The Health and Safety at Work etc Act 1974* Ch37 The Stationery Office
1974 ISBN 0 10 543774 3

9   *Chemical Agents Directive 98/24/EC* OJ L 131, 5.5.1998

10   *Explosive Atmospheres Directive 99/92/EC* (ATEX 137) OJ L23, 28.1.2000,
p57

11   *The Management of Health and Safety at Work Regulations 1999*
SI 1999/3242 The Stationery Office 1999 ISBN 0 11 085625 2

12   *The Fire Precautions Act 1971* The Stationery Office 1971
ISBN 0 10 544071 X

13   *The Fire Precautions (Workplace) Regulations 1997* SI 1997/1840
The Stationery Office 1997 ISBN 0110647386 (amended 1999)

14   *The Control of Substances Hazardous to Health Regulations 2002*
SI 2002/2677 The Stationery Office 2002 ISBN 0 11 042919 2

15   *The Control of Lead at Work Regulations 2002* SI 2002/2676
The Stationery Office 2002 ISBN 0 11 042917 6

16   *The Control of Asbestos at Work Regulations 2002* SI 2002/2675
The Stationery Office 2002 ISBN 0 11 042918 4

17   *The Confined Spaces Regulations 1997* SI 1997/1713 The Stationery Office
1997 ISBN 0 11 064643 6

18   *The Equipment and Protective Systems for Use in Potentially Explosive
Atmospheres Regulations 1996* SI 1996/192 The Stationery Office 1996
ISBN 0 11 053999 0 (as amended)

The Equipment and Protective Systems for use in Potentially Explosive Atmospheres (Amendment) Regulations 2001 The Stationery Office 1996 2001 SI 2001/3766 ISBN 0 11 038961 1

19   *ATEX Product Directive 94/9/EC* OJ L 100, 19.4.1994, p. 1

20   *The Provision and Use of Work Equipment Regulations 1998* SI 1998/2306 The Stationery Office 1998 ISBN 0 11 079599 7 (as amended)

21   *The Personal Protective Equipment at Work Regulations 1992* SI 1992/2966 The Stationery Office 1992 ISBN 0 11 025832 0

22   *The Petroleum (Consolidation) Act 1928* The Stationery Office 1928 ISBN 0 11 803433 2

23   *The Safety Representatives and Safety Committees Regulations 1977* SI 1977/500 The Stationery Office 1977 ISBN 0 11 70500 9

24   *The Health and Safety (Consultation with Employees) Regulations 1996* SI 1996/1513 The Stationery Office 1996 ISBN 0 11 054839 6

25   *Consulting employees on health and safety: A guide to the law* Leaflet INDG232 HSE Books 1996 (single copy free or priced packs of 15 ISBN 0 7176 1615 0)

26   *The Control of Major Accident Hazards Regulations 1999* SI 1999/743 The Stationery Office 1999 ISBN 0 11 082192 0

27   *The Offshore Installations (Prevention of Fire and Explosion, and Emergency Response) Regulations 1995* SI 1995/743 The Stationery Office 1995 ISBN 0 11 052751 8

28   *The Offshore Installations and Pipeline Works (Management and Administration) Regulations 1995* SI 1995/738 The Stationery Office 1995 ISBN 0 11 052735 6

29   *The Carriage of Dangerous Goods by Road Regulations 1996* SI 1996/2095 The Stationery Office 1996 ISBN 0 11 062926 4

30   *Pollution incident response planning: Environment Agency, Pollution Prevention Guidelines PPG 21* available free of charge by contacting the agencies on 08457 337700 or by email to environment-agency@DMSLTD.co.uk

31   *The Highly Flammable Liquids and Liquefied Petroleum Gases Regulations 1972* SI 1972/917 The Stationery Office 1972 ISBN 0 11 020917 6

32   *The Factories Act 1961* The Stationery Office 1961 ISBN 0 10 850027 6

33   *The Health and Safety (Enforcing Authority) Regulations 1998* SI 1998/494 The Stationery Office 1998 ISBN 0 11 065642 3

34   *The Chemicals (Hazard Information and Packaging for Supply) Regulations* SI 2002/1689 The Stationery Office 2002 ISBN 0 11 42419 0

35   *Approved classification and labelling guide. Chemicals (Hazard Information and Packaging for Supply) Regulations 2002. Guidance on Regulations* L131 (Fifth edition) HSE Books 2002 ISBN 0 7176 2369 6

36   *Approved supply list. Information approved for the classification and labelling of substances and preparations dangerous for supply. Chemicals (Hazard Information and Packaging for Supply) Regulations 2002. Approved list* L129 (Seventh edition) HSE Books 2002 ISBN 0 7176 2368 8

37   *Safe handling of combustible dusts. Precautions against explosions* HSE Books 2003 HSG103 ISBN 0 7176 2726 8

38   *Dust expert* Software programme developed by HSE and available from DNV Risk Management Software, Palace House, 3 Cathedral Street, London SE1 9DE, Tel 020 7716 6525. More information available at www2.dnv.com/software

39   EU Directive 67/548/EEC *The approximation of laws, regulations and administrative provisions relating to the classification, packaging and labelling of dangerous substances*

40   *Explosion protection systems. Method for determination of explosion indices of combustible dusts in air* BS 6713-1:1996 British Standards Institute

41   *Determination of the explosion characteristics of dust clouds Part1: Determination of the maximum explosion pressure* prEN14034 British Standards Institute

42   *The Workplace (Health, Safety and Welfare) Regulations 1992* SI 1992/3004 The Stationery Office 1992 ISBN 0 11 025804 5

43   *The Gas Appliances (Safety) Regulations 1995* SI 1995/1629 The Stationery Office 1995 ISBN 0 11 053337 2

44   *The Gas Safety (Installation and Use) Regulations 1998* SI 1998/245 The Stationery Office 1998 ISBN 0 11 079655 1

45   *The Explosives Act 1875* Ch17 The Stationery Office 1875 ISBN 0 11 802667 4

46   *European Agreement concerning the International Carriage of Dangerous Goods by Road 2003* ISBN 9211390788

47   *The Radioactive Materials (Road Transport) (Great Britain) Regulations 2002* SI 2002/1093 The Stationery Office 2002 ISBN 0 11 042248 1

48   *The Classification and Labelling of Explosives Regulations 1983* SI 1983/1140 The Stationery Office 1983 ISBN 0 11 037140 2

49   *The Packaging of Explosives for Carriage Regulations 1991* SI 1991/2097 The Stationery Office 1991 ISBN 0 11 015197 X

50   *The Carriage of Explosives by Road Regulations 1996* SI 1996/2093 The Stationery Office 1996 ISBN 0 11 062925 6

51   *The Carriage of Dangerous Goods (Classification, Packaging and Labelling) and Use of Transportable Pressure Receptacles Regulations 1996* SI 1996/2092 The Stationery Office 1996 ISBN 0 11 062923 X

52   *The Carriage of Dangerous Goods by Road (Driver Training) Regulations 1996* SI 1996/2094 The Stationery Office 1996 ISBN 0 11 062928 0

53   The Transport of Dangerous Goods (Safety Advisers) Regulations 1999
SI 1999/257 The Stationery Office 1999 ISBN 0 11 080434 1

54   International Carriage of Dangerous Goods by Rail ISBN 011552553X

55   Packaging and Labelling and Carriage of Radioactive Material by Rail
Regulations 2002 SI 2002/2099 The Stationery Office 2002
ISBN 0 11 042651 7

56   The Carriage of Dangerous Goods by Rail Regulations 1996 SI 1996/2089
The Stationery Office 1996 ISBN 0 11 062919 1

57   Technical Instructions for the safe transport of dangerous goods by air 2003/04
edition International Civil Aviation Organisation ISBN 92 9194 010 0
Available from Airplan Flight Equipment Ltd, 1A Ringway Trading Estate,
Shadowmoss Road, Manchester M22 5LH, Tel: 0161 499 0023,
Fax: 0161 499 0298, E-mail: enquiries@afeonline.com

58   The Air Navigation (Dangerous Goods) Regulations 2002 SI 2002/2786 The
Stationery Office 2002 ISBN 0 11 04297 10

59   International Maritime Dangerous Goods Code 2002 edition
International Maritime Organisation Product code ID200E Available at
www.imo.org/home.asp

60   The Merchant Shipping (Dangerous Goods and Marine Pollutants)
Regulations 1997 SI 1997/2367 The Stationery Office 1997
ISBN 0 11 064955 9

61   Management of health and safety at work. Management of Health and Safety
at Work Regulations 1999. Approved Code of Practice and guidance L21 (Second
edition) HSE Books 2000 ISBN 0 7176 2488 9

62   Functional safety of electrical/electronic/programmable electronic systems/safety
related systems BS EN 61508 British Standards Institute

63   Functional safety – Safety instrumented systems for the process industry sector
BS IEC 61511 British Standards Institute

64   Code of Practice Part 7: Storage of full and empty LPG cylinders and
cartridges LP Gas Association 1998 available from LP Gas Association,
Pavilion 16, Headlands Business Park, Salisbury Road, Ringwood, Hampshire
BH24 3PB or www.lpga.co.uk

65   Electrical apparatus for explosive gas atmospheres: Part 10 – Classification of
hazardous areas BS EN 60079-10:1996 British Standards Institute

66   Electrical apparatus for potentially explosive atmospheres – Pressurised
apparatus BS EN 50016 British Standards Institute

67   Fire safety. An Employers' Guide The Stationery Office 1999
ISBN 0 11 341229 0

68   Seven steps to successful substitution of hazardous substances HSG110
HSE Books 1994 ISBN 0 7176 0695 3

69   Designing and operating safe chemical reaction processes HSG143
HSE Books 2000 ISBN 0 7176 1051 9

70   *Equipment for use in the presence of combustible dusts. Part 3 - Classification of areas where combustible dusts are or may be present* BS EN 50281-3:2002 British Standards Institute

71   *Safe use and handling of flammable liquids* HSG140 HSE Books 1996 ISBN 0 7176 0967 7

72   *The storage of flammable liquids in containers* HSG51 (Second edition) HSE Books 1998 ISBN 0 7176 1471 9

73   *The storage of flammable liquids in tanks* HSG176 HSE Books 1998 ISBN 0 7176 1470 0

74   *Model Code of Safe Practice Part 15: Area classification code for installations handling flammable fluids* Institute of Petroleum 2002 (now the Energy Institute) ISBN 0 85293 223 5 Available from Portland Press Ltd, Commerce Way, Colchester CO2 8HP, Tel: 01206 796351

75   *Guidance for the design, construction, modification and maintenance of petrol filling stations* Institute of Petroleum (now the Energy Institute) and Association for Petroleum and Explosives Administration 1999 ISBN 0 85293 217 0 Available from Portland Press Ltd, Commerce Way, Colchester CO2 8HP, Tel: 01206 796351

76   *Code of practice Part 1: Bulk LPG storage at fixed installations* LP Gas Association 1998 available from LP Gas Association, Pavilion 16, Headlands Business Park, Salisbury Road, Ringwood, Hampshire BH24 3PB or www.lpga.co.uk

77   *Non-electrical equipment for potentially explosive atmospheres. Basic method and requirements* BS EN 13463-1:2001 British Standards Institute 2001

78   *The Dangerous Substances (Notification and Marking of Sites) Regulations* SI 1990/304 The Stationery Office 1990 ISBN 0 11 003304 3

79   *The Health and Safety (Safety Signs and Signals) Regulations 1996* SI 1996/341 The Stationery Office 1996 ISBN 0 11 054093 X

80   *Code of practice for control of undesirable static electricity. General considerations* BS 5958:1991-1 British Standards Institute
Code of practice for control of undesirable static electricity. Recommendations for particular industrial situations BS 5958:1991-1 British Standards Institute

81   *Electrostatics. Code of practice for the avoidance of hazards due to static electricity* PD CLC/TR 50404:2003 British Standards Institute

82   *The Health and Safety (First Aid) Regulations 1981* SI 1981/917 The Stationery Office 1981 ISBN 0 11 016917 4

83   *The Radiation (Emergency Preparedness and Public Information) Regulations 2001* SI 2001/2975 The Stationery Office 2001 ISBN 0 11 029908 6

84   *The Offshore Installations (Safety Representatives and Safety Committees) Regulations 1989* SI 1989/971 The Stationery Office 1989 ISBN 0 11 096971 5

85   *Successful health and safety management* HSG65 (Second edition) HSE Books 1997 ISBN 0 7176 1276 7

86 *The Celluloid and Cinematic Film Act 1922* The Stationery Office 1922 ISBN 0 10 850444 1

87 *The Petroleum Spirit (Motor Vehicles etc) Regulations 1929* The Stationery Office 1929 ISBN 0 11 100195 1

88 *Recreational Craft Directive 94/25/EC* OJ L 164, 30.6.1994, p. 15

89 *Notification of Installations Handling Hazardous Substances Regulations 1982* SI 1982/1357 The Stationery Office 1982 ISBN 0110273575

90 *The Petroleum (Liquid Methane) Order 1957* SI 1957/859 The Stationery Office 1957 ISBN 0 11 100276 1

91 *The Petroleum (Carbide of Calcium) Order 1929* The Stationery Office 1929 ISBN 0 11 100206 0

92 *The Petroleum (Carbide of Calcium) 1947* The Stationery Office 1947 ISBN 0 11 100412 8

93 *The Petroleum (Compressed Gases) Order 1930* The Stationery Office ISBN 0 11 100080 7

94 *The Petroleum Spirit (Plastic Containers) Regulations 1982* SI 1982/630 The Stationery Office 1982 ISBN 0 11 026630 7

95 *The Dangerous Substances in Harbour Areas Regulations 1987* SI 1987/37 The Stationery Office 1987 ISBN 0 11 076037 9

Further information

Dangerous Substances and Explosive Atmospheres Regulations 2002. A short guide for the offshore industry ON58 Available at www.hse.gov.uk/hid/osd/notices/on_58.htm

Printed and published by the Health and Safety Executive   12/03   C80